D0594081

of po
the ma,
foundly
starting
zation.
sion of
yet greater
vast changes
ductivity of
being. Her
technology
conquest

THE SCIENTIFIC REVOLUTION
AND WORLD POLITICS

THE ELIHU ROOT LECTURES

THE SCIENTIFIC REVOLUTION AND WORLD POLITICS

by
CARYL P. HASKINS

Published for the

COUNCIL ON FOREIGN RELATIONS

by

HARPER & ROW, Publishers

New York and Evanston

To E. F. H.

For whom this book was made

PREFACE

THE SUBSTANCE of what follows was given as the third series of Elihu Root Lectures for the Council on Foreign Relations in November and December of 1961.

Much has happened in the world since the lectures were delivered, and some revision of their detail seemed desirable. But no quality of our time is more striking than the contrast between the headlong pace and the often apparently random direction of the daily events that beat upon our lives and the constancy of those longer, deeper swells that lie beneath them, shaping major outlines of our history and determining major outlines of our foreign affairs. Some of those swells, obviously, respond importantly to the swift currents of science and technology. They are not new currents, relative to many others. Their direction, probably, has not changed greatly over the last few years. But as we are all aware, their magnitude, and so the variety and the pace of their effects, have increased almost beyond comprehension. This book attempts to scan, in brief and abbreviated compass, the nature and the direction of certain of those currents as they affect some aspects of the foreign policy of the United States today, and as they may be expected to influence it in the future.

My particular gratitude goes out to those colleagues and friends of the Council on Foreign Relations and of *Foreign Affairs* who have had so much to do with shaping the work in a multitude of aspects: most especially to Hamilton Fish Armstrong and Philip Quigg who brought much to those portions which appeared in *Foreign Affairs*, to Henry A. Wriston and to George

S. Franklin, Jr., to David MacEachron, W. Phillips Davison, Robert Valkenier and Mrs. Grace Darling whose comments on and criticism of the manuscript are beyond appreciation. And I owe a very special debt to my assistant, Miss Marjorie Walburn, without whose preparation of the typescript itself there would have been no manuscript.

CARYL P. HASKINS

CONTENTS

THE SCIENTIFIC REVOLUTION
AND WORLD POLITICS

1

INTRODUCTION:
DIMENSIONS
AND PARAMETERS

It is a particular fortune, and a special challenge, to address the pages that follow to an area of American foreign policy which so little as a quarter of a century ago might still have been deemed of minor importance—the impact upon our foreign affairs of the forces of world science and world technology. After the history of three great wars dominated by military technology and a prolonged cold war especially characterized by thinking in the technical sphere, it appears far from minor today. Yet so new is it in our experience, and so manifold and commanding are its present proportions, that we are still in a literal sense groping in our efforts to come to grips with it.

The world of science and technology and that of foreign policy seem superficially far apart. The kinds of understanding involved in each are often widely different, the skills required seem disparate, the training and the temperament to implement them have traditionally appeared wholly distinct. And so it is not always easy to recognize their points of junction and of coincidence.

Yet perhaps more than any other people in the world, Americans are historically well equipped to appreciate these conjunctions, by virtue of the intimate relation which we have always recognized between science and technology and our domestic public affairs. One hundred and thirty years ago, in the presidency of John Quincy Adams, it would already have seemed wholly natural to an American to couple the waxing inner strength of his country with the contemporary lusty growth of a still primitive American technology and science. John Quincy Adams himself when Secretary of State saw nothing incongruous in personally preparing for the Congress his *Report Upon Weights and Measures,* uniting with the responsibilities of statesmanship a deep and abiding personal concern with science. Through all the following years to the present we have continued to take it for granted that in essential elements of our domestic political philosophy and of the administrative structure of our government, no less than in our intellectual orientation and in the sinews of our internal material strength, we are deeply committed and indebted to the technical and the scientific way. The whole history and pattern of our domestic institutions, indeed, vividly reflects this scientific and technical element. Correspondingly, our mechanisms of government for organizing and channeling the forces of science and technology in the service of our internal strength are extensive, sophisticated, and on the whole vigorous. If they sometimes creak and grind, if we are frequently preoccupied with aspects of their current inadequacies, this is primarily because of the gravity of the challenges that are continually presented to them, and the wind-swift speed with which those challenges magnify and change. In response, these mechanisms have today entered phases of growth so vastly augmented as sometimes to seem almost different in kind. But basically they are the products of a long and continuous evolution.

Even as late as the Second World War, we did not sense anything like so obvious and deep a connection between the foreign policy of the United States *per se* and the provinces of science and technology. But with that war, and ever since, the most fearsome military aspects of the relation have been thrust upon us with steadily increasing emphasis. From wartime radar to napalm incendiary bombs to atomic explosives of the Hiroshima class, from the fifty-megaton Soviet blast over Novaya Zemlya on the thirtieth of October 1961 and the reported leviathan hundred-megaton Russian weapon to the current sophisticated lower-yield nuclear weapons of greater versatility with which we are more

familiar, from Whittle engines to modern jet aircraft to high pay-
load space-range rocketry, from warships to nuclear-powered sub-
marines, the awesome technical tools of the military art have
advanced, never for a moment in recent years leaving us unheed-
ing of this poignant facet of the relation of technology and science
to foreign affairs and to world power.

Though this keen awareness is barely more than twenty years
old, our experience has been intensive and we have already
achieved some remarkable structures of government organization
in its service, following the example and the tradition of the
Office of Scientific Research and Development of World War II.
To patterns initiated in that intense period of practical appreciation we owe some major contemporary structures within our
government which play an important part in linking science and
technology with foreign policy. The Office of Naval Research, the
National Science Foundation, the Atomic Energy Commission,
and in a later day and as a natural outgrowth, the position of
Special Assistant to the President for Science and Technology,
the President's Science Advisory Committee, the Federal Council
of Science and Technology, and, most pointedly, the Office of the
Science Adviser in the Department of State, all are deeply concerned among other things with aspects of scientific and technical
knowledge in relation to foreign affairs.

But there is a further implication of science and technology in
American foreign affairs to which our attention has been seriously
turned only very recently. It is possible, indeed, that at no earlier
point in our history than the last three years could an American
Secretary of State, with any real hope of general attention and
understanding, have used the words of Dean Rusk at the Centennial Celebration of the Massachusetts Institute of Technology:

It seems to me rather curious at the present moment, and perhaps
it is just a moment, that the nations and peoples of the earth seem to
be pinning their hopes on the possibilities of scientific and technical
development for the satisfaction of basic human needs. . . . It may be
that we have a chance for a time to get a job done which will implant

that idea deeply into the consciousness of man and put us into a position to give up the temptations of predatory seizure of resources elsewhere. But if these expectations are not satisfied and we cannot make tolerable advances, one can see down the road the renewal of pressures for more lands, more resources, and great hazards to the peace of the world.

There are complex reasons why this aspect of the role of science and technology in foreign affairs has lagged so significantly behind our keen appreciation of the domestic and the military facets. Some of them, clearly, lie within ourselves and follow from the very state of our society. But others relate to massive changes which have occurred in recent years in the whole topography of the world itself. For it is literally true that major patterns of power and frameworks of strategy and decision against which American policies were set in the periods of the first and second great wars, and even of the opening phases of the cold war era, no longer *exist*. They have been replaced in part by some quite different ones which are likely, given a world spared from nuclear holocaust, to endure in general outline and to grow and become more evident for years to come. The genesis of these new patterns and the ways in which they will develop in the future have been —and are, to a degree which only now we are coming to appreciate fully—the consequences of that same scientific and technical revolution which in a very different mode dominated the years of warfare. But their broader implications are vastly different in the setting of a new world, and today we are still all too ill-equipped to deal with them sensitively and firmly and generally effectively at the level of government.

Predominant among the recent changes in the political structure of the world, one which has already become of first importance for us and the significance of which will surely grow steadily over the coming decades, is the rapidly accelerating diffusion of global power with which we live. A world which at the end of the second great war we correctly estimated to be essentially bipolar in terms of power—a configuration to which we grew so accustomed that we have continued to regard it in that light almost to the present—had in fact begun to alter significantly at least a decade ago. The emergence of Yugoslavia from Soviet control in 1948; the widening breach between the Soviet Union and China; the new independence of India and Indonesia, Burma, Ceylon, Egypt; the nascent African states; the rapid recrudescence of Japan to the first rank of modern world powers, and last and greatest, the dramatic strides of Western Europe—all these developments emphasize how much, in the arena of world politics, the brittle bipolar concentration of power which haunted us for so long was being confronted with a dramatically increasing plurality, stridently expounded by General de Gaulle. That pluralism affects more than geography. Very conceivably, it may involve not only a significant change in the scale of world power in times of comparative peace, but with that change, and reinforcing it, a related evolution in the nature and the comparative weight of various survival factors for a nation in time of war. For with the development of massive atomic arsenals in our day and the potentialities for immense and almost instantaneous destruction that they carry, the relative sizes of stockpiles of highly sophisticated nuclear weapons possessed by competing major states conceivably could prove of less ultimate practical significance than the capacity to maintain a continuing—even though a far less sophisticated—capability *after* massive initial salvos. With that capability, too, there must be associated the continuing ability for innovation in war being waged—the ability to exploit, in the interests of defense, every last drop from remaining natural resources. This, of course, is by no means a new idea. But in the full context of contemporary weapons and modern warfare, it introduces quite a fresh dimension to our thinking.

Another element of the same pattern may suggest quite different, and possibly contradictory considerations. One can ask the poignant question: "How compatible is the dispersion of major nuclear power among states with the development of a plurality of nations in the world?" To what degree is the nuclear bipolarity that still characterizes the world in which we live—however brief the future in which this may continue to be true—actually a significant stabilizing factor beneath whose protecting shadow other forms of diffusion of power among nations may proceed? Conversely, would the widespread distribution of militarily significant nuclear arsenals among many states actually encourage a retreat from a polycentric world? Would small nations whose material resources could not cope with the exhausting economic drains imposed by the manufacture or maintenance of those arsenals be impelled to seek safety in the shelter of larger ones, even at considerable costs of autonomy? Or would they, alternatively, strive to achieve an economic stature which allowed them to attain the status of significant nuclear powers through political consolidations among themselves? Such questions are so difficult that it is dangerous at this distance even to hazard answers to them. Yet before long we may have the beginning of the evidence. Such significant and perhaps often contradictory changes in the configuration of our world, in the realms of military strategy and tactics among others, are obviously ones for which modern technology has been, or in future will be, primarily responsible.

But the influences of science and technology in our day extend to a deeper level, and one possibly much more meaningful in its total implications for humanity. For they also bespeak possible vast changes in the strength and productivity of states in terms of conquest over nature and in terms of human welfare and human potential. The same leverage of science and technology which has influenced that growing pluralism of military power can also strengthen and stabilize a political and economic plurality through its contributions to the increased productive potentials of states, and, yet more significantly, to the increased individual welfare of their citizens. Finally, those more profound aspects of science involving the search for its own sake of truth about the natural world may well bring to men of states which historically have stood outside the original scientific revolution of the West intellectual and emotional and spiritual returns fully comparable in our time with those which so dramatically characterized the scientific revolution in Western Europe three hundred years ago.

Such tremendous goals as these will not be achieved facilely or simply, neither at short ranges of time, nor without the prior attainment of a host of prerequisite conditions in many new societies. But even their possibility in our day, and the magnitude of their implications in terms both of human values and of social and political welfare, are impressive. It may be no exaggeration to emphasize that the very political future of our globe, now and for a considerable time ahead, may rest importantly with success on two fronts: the uniting of the forces of the free world into larger entities which, while highly flexible politically, can bring their weighty moral and intellectual and political forces to bear most effectively in shaping and guarding the future; and the successful transition of the many new nations to the point where they can make their own political choices with the responsible judgments of maturity. On both these fronts technology and science have important parts to play. For not only is it universally clear today that in science and technology, in no small measure, lie significant keys to wealth and power in the world. It is also clear that science by its very nature can be one of the most international of all human activities, dealing as it does with knowledge and understanding that inherently transcend both natural and man-made boundaries, and with the control and use of natural forces whose common deployment and the enjoyment of whose common benefits can provide important binding ties among states. Given the achievement and the maintenance of military security at appropriate levels, these human and political potentials of science and technology in our day may well be the most important of all their implications for American foreign policy.

〽〽〽

THE EMPHASIS in this book, then, will be upon the forces of science and technology in relation to the internal strength and development of peoples, in their binding force among peoples, and in their significance in various sorts of societies. At the outset, we will consider especially some aspects of the significance first of technology and then of science for the emerging nations of the world, now approaching a position to appreciate and make use of their promise and their power—and equally, to be liable to their dangers. For the purposes of specific discussion, this class of nations will be defined in a rather unconventional way, which incidentally reveals two important personal biases of the author. These biases will affect the whole approach, and so they should be presented explicitly at the very beginning.

The first bias is that the scientific revolution of the West—the revolution, especially, comprehending the years from Galileo and Copernicus to the years following Newton—has a meaning for the present day and for the new nations which is far more than historical. It is indeed of great contemporary significance, and this, among others, for three compelling reasons. First, it brought to the West, and can now be expected to bring to others in the future, a world view so radically new that it may well be transforming to the peoples who experience it. Second, and related, is the important fact that it brought for the first time, and may now bring again elsewhere, the real conviction that not only can significant aspects of the laws of nature be understood by man, but they can be effectively used for man's practical gain. These things seem obvious to us today, with our long scientific history and our scientific sophistication. Yet they embody the precise opposite of the pre-Renaissance view in Western Europe. Before the scientific revolution the basic view of the European alchemist and astrologer was that power over nature was to be obtained by outguessing and outwitting her, not by first understanding her laws and then working in accord with them. The vast and vital shifts of philosophy in this context that the Renaissance brought to the West may still be far from obvious today in some parts of the world, and it is easy to underestimate the excitement and the release that such a metamorphosis of view can bring.

The third reason, more fundamental than the other two, in some measure includes them both. Our post-Renaissance society, so dominated by science and technology, sets an overriding value upon the search for truth, defined not only in the context of viable and intellectually satisfying propositions, but, at last, as the faithful description of our natural and our swift-changing social worlds as we can best delineate them. We are committed at a very deep level to the proposition that the search for truth in that definition is an extremely important end of our whole existence. Now from this acceptance of truth as an overriding value there follows inevitably a powerful commitment to the scientific way. And this commitment brings with it other social consequences quite as fundamental and universal. For, so long as a society considers truth in this light and so long as the search for it has a high value, *ipso facto* it harbors powerful incentives to remain both dynamic and flexible. A society so committed is compelled for that very reason to set a high value upon, and to give protection to, the independent and original mind whatever its other characteristics, for it is upon such minds that the effective search for truth depends. This is a powerful safeguard of originality and individuality in our society—surely one of the most powerful that can be provided. In a very real sense, this notion of truth and this high valuing of the search for it, both so closely linked to the scientific concept, do much to ensure that a society harboring them remains flexible and preserves, quite literally, the power to evolve. Conversely, the truly traditional society, in which all knowledge is in a literal sense close to revealed knowledge—the society firmly committed to the proposition that truth is ordained and fixed—is by that fact dangerously removed from the well-springs of renewal and the power of evolution, and this may be its basic handicap as it seeks to enter the modern world.

The transition from one viewpoint to the other, which all really traditional societies must face and must accomplish in a frighteningly short time if they are to survive and prosper, may not seem either very radical or very difficult to achieve. In fact the exact contrary is true. The degree to which such a change constitutes a social revolution of the most genuine sort, and the extreme importance that it be navigated effectively and with a minimum of the trauma which inevitably attends social upheavals of that caliber, will be a major underlying theme of all that follows.

The second bias is of a different character, but nonetheless is closely linked to the first. It is that, closely woven and closely interdependent as are science and technology in our civilization today, and much as we take their intimate relationship for granted in all that we do, they are actually significantly different both in origin and in nature. It may be extremely important to bear this fact in mind, especially when considering the new nations.

※※※

So WE may categorize as "new" those nations of the world which, throughout all but their most recent history, have stood largely apart from the currents of the scientific revolution of the West. It is certainly more than accidental that the nations which are "new" by this criterion are also, in general, underdeveloped. But this relationship is complex, and it is possible to cite societies in the modern world which are at a strikingly modest level of development, yet of which the converse proposition is not true. It is the nations that are new in the sense of exposure to the influences of that scientific revolution that we shall first consider in their relation to science and technology.

Then we may pass to a consideration of science and technology in relation to societies that have now crossed this historical watershed. That category will include all those peoples who, either from direct experience or through a relatively early and continuing secondary exposure, in the main have understood and have come to take for granted the deeper implications of the scientific revolution. This class has a large and miscellaneous membership, varying widely in other of its characteristics. It includes nations that are "intermediate" in technical, economic, and political senses, like many Afro-Asian states and some in Latin America. It includes, in certain aspects of their scientific climate and scientific needs, some nations of Western Europe. In some aspects of climate and needs, it includes our own country.

Then following these considerations, we shall turn to some facets of scientific and technical matters as factors for international solidarity in Western European society. Finally, we shall attempt, in very brief and summary fashion, to comment upon some aspects of a most controversial and vexing, and withal fascinating, matter: the nature and position of science and technology in the great Communist countries, and the implications that may dwell therein for their future evolution, for the free world, and, to a degree, for science itself.

I. THE NEW NATIONS

2

TECHNOLOGY
AND THE
NEW NATIONS

In 1945 fifty-one states had set their hand to the Charter of the United Nations. In September 1961 the century mark in the membership of the U.N. was attained with the admission of Sierra Leone. By May of 1963, with the admission of Kuwait, the membership stood at no less than one hundred and eleven. This precipitate growth bears as dramatic witness as anything could to the political dynamism and weight of the new nations of the world, now and for the future. Neglecting the iron curtain countries, the less developed nations comprehend today approximately two-fifths of the population of the globe. Their lands include approximately a third of its surface. In population, in territory, in potential political influence over the years to come, they represent one of the most significant elements among the world's peoples. The average *per capita* income of the approximately one billion people who live within these lands may range from approximately $50 to little more than $100 per year, contrasting with the condition of the approximately four hundred million people living in the industrial world of Europe and North America, Australia, and the advanced portions of South America and South Africa, with an average *per capita* income of perhaps $1,000 annually.

For a majority of these peoples the overwhelming needs are starkly practical at present. The control of hunger, the conquest of epidemic disease, the elementary development of natural resources are obvious imperatives. These countries stand in the most acute need of appropriate and developed technologies. *Today* their demands on science must be addressed almost wholly to its pragmatic side. But it is not to be forgotten that, if those demands are fulfilled with any degree of success, tomorrow they will surely wish to participate in the continuing scientific revolution of the wider world outside their borders. As that time arrives, the problem of providing effective scientific and technical aid may become even more subtle than it is at present—and it will, if possible, be even more critical. We shall consider this matter at greater length in the next chapter.

In many ways we are inherently well placed to aid the new nations of the world with appropriate technologies to strengthen their economies, and few areas in the whole field of foreign aid can be more important. At this level the matter seems at first sight relatively straightforward in principle, however massive and complex in practice. In fact, however, as the experience of the last years has vividly emphasized, it is fairly studded with basic questions, relating as much to underlying concepts as to matters of execution. Some of the most formidable cluster around judgments as to what constitutes true relevance in the technologies sought by the new nations, or that we seek to bring them.

The population of the world today approximates three billion people. By 1980 it will perhaps have reached four billion; and a projected figure for the year 2000 is seven billion. A considerable share of that increase, amounting to as high a figure as two per cent per annum, is taking place in the new countries. At the same time, and for a variety of reasons, there are strong pressures leading to a steady widening, rather than a narrowing, of the economic gap between the highly developed and the underdeveloped nations. It is quite clear that technologies which are relevant to the needs of the new countries must differ in many respects from those appropriate to the advanced industrial ones and that in a substantive sense the simpler and more elementary fields are likely to be critical. The effective areas of concern and avenues of action here may not be those that appeal most strongly to our own deep-laid instincts for the dramatic, the novel, and the massive. Extractive technologies, technologies of civil engineering and planning, technologies concerned with the development and exploitation of appropriate and available energy sources will inevitably bear especially heavily upon the needs of the new nations.

High among the priorities, obviously, lie techniques of food production, including agronomy and crop and animal improvement and soil science. It should be technically possible to feed the explosively expanding populations of the new countries on areas already available for cultivation, given modern husbandry. Indeed, a recent report of the Director General of the Food and Agriculture Organization of the United Nations indicated that Asia is currently managing to increase food production one per cent faster than its rise in population, albeit both the quantity and quality remain grossly inadequate over-all. Moreover, the volume of Asia's agricultural exports increased seven per cent in the last decade.

The problem, however, goes far beyond that of agronomic method or of immediate technology. For example, India is outstanding among the low-income countries of the world in the number and variety of her research and technological institutions, among them many devoted wholly or in part to problems of food production. More than a dozen research centers are coordinated by the Indian Council of Agricultural Research, including special institutes for research on rice, forestry, fishes, veterinary problems, dairy problems. The Council of Scientific and Industrial Research, well established and very active for many years under the Ministry of Scientific Research and Cultural Affairs, operates almost thirty research institutions dealing with the application of science to the development problems of the country, including a central research institute in food technology. Probably no one of the developing countries at the lower economic levels possesses so great a potential to determine immediate relevances in specific technologies.

And yet how very much broader vital questions of relevance

can be was well illustrated in that nation by quite a different kind of inquiry. A few years ago the Indian government adviser P. C. Mahalanobis assembled some figures relating to nutrition which are very instructive in a more general context. It was estimated at that time that an added production in India of about 700,000 tons of food grains would be required each year merely to maintain a constant standard of living in the expanding population, let alone to increase it at all. To import the required amount of grain from abroad would demand approximately $400 million annually of scarce Indian foreign exchange. To achieve the same result by cultivating the grains locally would require the use of roughly 300,000 tons of a standard chemical fertilizer, such as ammonium sulfate. The import cost of this would be in the range of $140 million. To build a large fertilizer plant to make the ammonium sulfate on which to raise the grains would cost about $60 million of foreign exchange. Finally, to establish an organization to build the fertilizer plant to make the fertilizer to raise the grains would cost still less, and this, other things being equal, was obviously by far the preferable course.

These figures, taken merely as an illustration, emphasize an important general criterion of the relevance of technologies for the new countries in a purely practical sense. How vital such relevance may be is suggested by the fact that, despite the gain of one per cent in food production over population increase reported for Asia by the Food and Agricultural Organization last year—a most remarkable achievement—with corresponding gain in agricultural exports, such exports in 1962 actually purchased less in terms of manufactured goods than did the figure for 1959. Thus conservation of monetary exchange is a particularly vital factor in the new countries, to offset as much as possible the strong pressures driving to widen the economic gap between the developed and the underdeveloped. And the further back in agricultural production the basic processes can be started, the less will be the cost in a capital-scarce economy. But at the same time, the further back in the production chain the investment comes, the longer must be the time of waiting, and exploding populations make it vital that the wait be no longer than is absolutely necessary. There are delicate questions of judgment here, and they will differ in every case.

There are further and often subtle criteria of relevance. For instance, the scarcity of capital in the new countries obviously puts pressures on technologies in general to carry the lowest practicable investment and development costs. Yet this rule may not always apply in specific cases. Thus it may sometimes be desirable to make a heavy capital investment to establish an industry—such as the tool industry—in a new country even if the unit cost of the products of such an undertaking proves significantly higher, for the time being at least, than that of similar products purchased ready-made abroad. Here the relevant investment, in good part, may lie in the establishment of the industry itself and the consequent training and intellectual molding and reshaping of a substantial body of workers within the country. It may be worth a high price to a new nation thus to introduce at one stroke the mainsprings of an industrial civilization. Other similar contradictions can plague observers overly given to generalize in this context. For example, it seems self-evident that the abundance of unskilled manpower relative to capital so characteristic of many of the new nations requires that relevant technologies should maximize the productiveness of existing human resources rather than conserve those resources by replacing manpower with machines. In food production, for example, technologies in such nations should be directed primarily toward securing an increase in yield per acre rather than in output per man. On the other hand, in underpopulated new nations like some of those in Africa the challenge may be the very opposite. It is clear that each nation must constitute a special case, requiring particular analysis.

But it is surely a safe generality that the scarcity of capital so typical of nearly all the new nations does imperatively dictate very special adaptations of production technology to conserve that capital; and in devising and effecting such adaptations may lie one of the richest fields for western technical aid to the new nations. Sometimes these adaptations may seem so minor and detailed as to appear, at first glance, almost trivial; and yet their ultimate benefits may prove large indeed. Recently, for example, the Pan American Union engineered and developed a simple mechanical two-man press, designed to fabricate a sturdy building block from a compressed and solidified mixture of mud and lime or cement. It is an invention that would hardly attract attention at home. Yet in the new countries it brings promise of greatly aiding an essential labor which for countless millennia has consumed an immense amount of manual effort—and of doing this, moreover, with a very low capital investment. Again, an adaptation of well-known chemical engineering procedures to produce methane gas for lighting and heating and the generation of power from waste materials in primitive villages has been tested both in Kenya and India and found highly effective, actually also improving the value of the waste as fertilizer. An older, but strikingly similar, illustration of the same point is provided by the design of primitive plants for nitrogen production from human wastes undertaken through the Office of Scientific Research and Development and used in mainland China early in World War II.

These are detailed examples, but similar principles operate on a much more general scale. To take the example of grain production in India, for instance, the establishment of a single large fertilizer plant would almost certainly lie well beyond the capital capacity of many of the new nations. But it may sometimes be true that efficient smaller plants to achieve the same ends will come within the capital range of the private entrepreneur, inside or outside the country. In some of the new nations small plants, tailor-made to local conditions, might well be able to accomplish feats of food production which would otherwise be quite impossible. In this field may also lie attractive possibilities for private investment in such nations.

In general, it will be important both for us and for the new nations to recognize that they should enter the technological field at a stage corresponding to an earlier period in the industrial revolution of the West—a period when, likewise, small plants were the rule. The requirements then were very different from those demanding the huge capital-intensive plants which are frequently, if not usually, most economical in an advanced society.

In estimating the needs of the new nations we should generally be wary of complex and striking technologies which may so easily promise more than they can accomplish, bringing that initial rise of hope and expectation and their subsequent dashing which can be so disillusioning and dangerous. An especially vivid example of this may be that of the "peaceful atom" in relation to the new nations. In the context of the intermediate nations, with their needs for relatively sophisticated research and research training, or in the milieu of the hoped-for needs of the new nations some years hence, radioisotopes, research reactors, and power reactors clearly have or will have their place, especially in view of improvements in the use of nuclear fuels which we may anticipate. But in the context of the current practical technical needs of the emerging countries the situation is quite different. It is easy to see today—by hindsight—that the Atoms for Peace program which we heralded with such enthusiasm in 1954 may on balance actually have rendered a disservice to the new nations. First, it had the effect of focusing attention unduly on one special sector of technology which, in the absence of serious research and evaluation of its special applicability for their needs, could not be anything like so relevant for the emerging countries as some other areas. Second, and perhaps more important, our own enthusiasm was bound to raise hopes which, at the present stage, could only be disappointed. How difficult it is for even a huge and an enormously populous country with a highly sophisticated intellectual tradition and intensive drive, but without an adequate industrial and technical base, to take rapid and effective advantage of the possibilities of nuclear energy—even in its military aspects—may, curiously, be illustrated by the current situation of China so far as we know it.

There is an important corollary of these considerations that we are apt to miss in the perspective of our own advanced technical, scientific, and industrial background. Both we and the new nations must understand that in general the powerful advanced novel technologies which we may expect from the industrial nations in ever-mounting volume over the years to come are not necessarily likely to be of significant help to the newer countries until they have themselves achieved a roughly comparable technical and industrial base. On the contrary, until that time the very existence of such technologies in the advanced countries may actually widen rather than narrow the existing economic gap between them and the emerging nations. That prospect need not be disheartening in itself, but failure on either side to remember it can easily lead to dangerous courses and bitter disillusionments.

Such definitions of relevance in the technologies most urgent to the new nations do not suggest that the knowledge to implement them lies at the frontiers of scientific advance in the industrial nations of the West. Indeed, it is likely that more basic information appropriate to the needs of the new nations is presently available in the stores of the industrial countries than can be effectively put to use for many years to come. The problem here is not one of research. But in a sense it is yet more formidable. It is a problem of discovery, of sensible and sensitive selection, and, above all, of adaptation to the peculiar and individual requirements of each nation, each people, each region. In most of the new countries there will be at least a few men generally familiar with technical matters who can seize upon the world's store of such knowledge, can with some assistance abstract appropriately from it, and, under favorable circumstances, can adapt such elements successfully to the needs of their societies. When the corps of such men is adequate in numbers and relatively sophisticated in outlook, the task of aid may resolve itself primarily to placing a general store of the appropriate information and the means for implementing it at their command and providing any advice which may be welcome in its adaptation. This is a serious and subtle enough undertaking in itself, requiring a high order of skill and devotion, as well as of quality and training, among those responsible for it. But it is not, basically, an unfamiliar task.

In far too many cases, however, technically sophisticated personnel are still extremely rare in the new nations. It is of the highest importance that the numbers of such personnel be augmented as rapidly as possible through appropriate secondary training, bearing always in mind, of course, the concomitant dangers of too-rapid specialization. So vital is the matter that radical measures should probably be taken in this direction by governments of new states even, when necessary, at the cost of short-term sacrifices in education at both primary and university levels, and even at the cost of some delay in attaining the alluring and undoubtedly important goal of universal literacy in the nation.

In this connection, there is already available in a number of the new states an important potential source of auxiliary technical training which should not be overlooked. Private corporations from advanced industrial nations operating in these countries may well find it to their own long-term interest, as it will certainly be to that of the host countries themselves, to embark upon what has been called a "planned wastage" of personnel. In any event such companies, by the very nature of their undertakings, must find it to their interest to provide technical education for their employees to some degree. If they are willing deliberately to undertake the technical training of a somewhat larger cadre of workers than they can use directly, anticipating that these trainees will go elsewhere, the costs need not be large but the proportionate increase of technical knowledge in the new countries where they work can be most significant. It is both refreshing and revealing to recall that it was not in formal training institutes that the men of Western Europe gained the technical knowledge that propelled the industrial revolution. It was not in such an environment that Josiah Wedgwood carved upon the bench of a careless potter, "This work will not do for J. Wedgwood." It was on the floors of small factories and in the environs of modest production plants that such education flourished. Here again, the new countries may be wise in attempting at first to follow some of the earlier courses in the historical evolution of the technology of Western Europe.

But under the present circumstances of the new nations a preponderant share of the burdens of selection, adaptation, and introduction of relevant technologies must inevitably rest with the donors, and the effectiveness with which these things are done will largely determine the success of our efforts at technical aid. And the effort is not only demanding. It is also risky. For lack of skillful and effective approaches may involve more than simple inefficiency. There is the real risk that it could spell disaster far more serious than if the attempt had never been made at all. Few stronger arguments could be advanced for the heavy reliance, in our current programs for development assistance overseas, upon a well-organized and effective structure of research and development particularly tailored to this end and with this end as its principal objective—a program and an organization charged with a continuing professional concern for identification of needs and wants, the adaptation of knowledge and techniques, the conduct of appropriate experiments, the education and training of special field personnel in the programs relating to the requirements of the new nations.

Few challenges to the whole pattern of our foreign aid are more severe than this. There is not only the danger of offering too-advanced, too-glittering, or otherwise poorly adapted technologies. There is the equally grave danger of forgetting that in all programs of technical aid an indispensable complement to success must be the internal will of the recipients to develop their own technical frontiers. Without such will, without a political climate which is at least tolerant to its expression and disposed to implement it, technical aid may bring in its train the same hazards that we have learned in recent years to associate in the economic field with monetary aid uncritically applied. And it must be remembered, in this connection, that among the past or the contemporary political leaders of the developing countries, only those of India and Israel have had extensive scientific training in their educational backgrounds.

This aspect of foreign aid must inherently bring—as indeed it is bringing—severe problems of organization and administration at the level of the federal government. It is quite possible that they do not all belong there. The interesting suggestion has recently been made that there may be profitable regions to explore in the design and administration of technical aid programs for the new nations directly at the level of the states. It is significant, indeed, that in many ways the technical problems in the new nations often match the problems of American state governments more closely than they do those of the federal establishment. An extremely significant element in this general approach and one which has expanded greatly in recent years, though often without sufficient organization or coordination, is the role of the state universities in overseas technical and scientific assistance. The effectiveness and importance of their activities is such as to merit much attention and support in the future.

$$\mathcal{SSS}$$

BUT the whole issue of technical aid to the newer nations poses squarely some much broader—and inescapable—questions relating to general federal policy. For example, how do its needs bear upon the total distribution of the federal technical effort? The implications reach quite as far as our own plans for the conquest of space. One significant query to which we should pay most careful attention might run: "In the vision of those new countries that view the world upon which they are entering with interests and from backgrounds often quite different from our own, is it leadership on vast and spectacular and sophisticated frontiers of exploration and power that will be most useful and impressive to them, or is it demonstrated leadership in technologies more relevant to their own practical needs, coupled with genuine and evident willingness and care and insight in making them available?" Clearly there can never be a simple answer to so broad and many-sided a question. Even our basic judgment of how to partition our efforts between such vastly disparate extremes must vary with circumstances, and from time to time. But it will be important to keep the grave significance of such choices constantly in our thinking, and to remind ourselves frequently that our own technological resources—in material terms but more especially in terms of men—are no more unlimited than are our economic ones. Indeed they are actually more limited because slower and more difficult to augment. Comparatively wealthy as we are in them, we are not wealthy enough simultaneously to do all things well on the vast scale that the contemporary world demands.

3

THE NEW NATIONS
AND THE
SCIENTIFIC REVOLUTION

B<small>UT VITAL</small> as relevant technologies are for the new nations, in the end they will not be enough. The new nations will need an indigenous, living science of their own, however limited in volume or in scope. This is admittedly a controversial proposition. There can be few more dangerous misconceptions in the whole field of technical and scientific aid to the new nations, indeed, than the idea of science as a magic wand which, waved over them, will cure ills whose basis lies in a complex of social, economic, and industrial factors of which science is but one element. We need continually to be sensitive to this. And yet the proposition is, I think, one of gravity and truth, for reasons which may become apparent.

The argument takes as its basis an important distinction between the nature of technology and of post-Newtonian science. It implies that, closely interlocked as they are in the modern lives of industrial peoples, they nonetheless differ in important ways relevant to the present context—a judgment reflecting the second bias set out in the Introduction. Since that bias conditions a good deal of what follows, it requires both verification and illustration. Before proceeding with the main theme, therefore, it may be worth-while to introduce a short historical digression relating to the circumstances of the technological and scientific revolutions as history has recently illumined them. It is a digression which may not be irrelevant to practical questions. Indeed, the picture which it draws may be rather profoundly illuminating in their context.

Modern historical research has revealed the truly immense age of developed technology, and emphasizes that, closely as modern science and technology are interwoven today and much as we often think of technology as the product of modern scientific effort, historically the two modes were quite separate in their origins. Archaeological findings of recent years make it very clear that man's revolution in technology antedated the scientific revolution by several millennia. Indeed, the technical revolution was probably coeval with the development of the great prehistoric urban centers of Asia and Africa and China. In Mesopotamia, in Egypt, in Babylon, in Crete, in northern India, the evidence is unmistakable that three thousand years ago men lived in cities at least as well planned and serviced as many of their counterparts in the same regions today. It was during these centuries, indeed, that Asian technical ingenuity seems to have reached its height. Paper was invented in China in the first century A.D., the magnetic compass in the third, printing with movable type in the eighth. In the fifteenth century districts and counties in China were equipped with rain gauges. Such achievements, including the invention of explosives and of an accurate escapement device for clock mechanisms, leave no doubt of the extraordinary achievements in invention, technology, and engineering that flowered in China at a period when the West was still essentially barbaric.

During this period in China, it would seem that almost every favorable condition prevailed, not only for the continuing development of a powerful practical technology, but for a scientific revolution too. There were skilled craftsmen in abundance; there was a wealthy and cultured segment of society with ample leisure; there was a skillfully maintained peace and order much of the time; there was a generous accumulation of capital. A practical science certainly flourished, involving some remarkable developments in measurement, in mathematics applied to measuring procedures, in geology, in observational astronomy. There are, for example, accurate accounts of eclipses, and extensive star catalogues recorded from the later Chinese Chou Dynasty, earlier than 200 B.C. Yet all this was not enough. It was in Europe, ill-equipped as it appeared to be, that the real revolution in scientific philosophy occurred.

Why this should have been so, why a true Asian scientific revolution never came, must stand among the great and important enigmas of history. Such a fundamental and unanswered question emphasizes our basic lack of understanding both of the processes of scientific revolution and of the underlying requirements for it. But pointed observations can be drawn from the events themselves. Significant among them are the long separation in time between the technological and the scientific revolutions in the world, amounting to three thousand years or more, and the fact that, whereas the technical revolution takes its deepest roots from the East and can therefore be expected to be a familiar phenomenon the world over, the scientific revolution, in its modern philosophic form, originally never touched the East at all.

In lesser measure, this curious separation between technology and post-Newtonian science existed even in the geographical cradle of the scientific revolution, and persisted there until well after the death of Newton. In Europe as in Asia, to be sure, a practical science and technology were early associated and interdependent. It can have been no accident that the years of conquest and of rapidly expanding oceanic trade were also the years when the first telescopes were designed, and the scientific study of optics and hydraulics preoccupied men's minds and so greatly influenced the course of natural philosophy. It was no accident, surely, that the mathematics of insurance and the computation of rates of interest underwent a great development in the later years of the Renaissance, when the commerce of the city-states was expanding so rapidly. But though this side of European science was firmly rooted in technology, and though some of the earliest European scientific societies were formally dedicated to improvements in the practical arts, technology remained distinct in a very fundamental sense from science in its revolutionary Newtonian garb.

From the outset, the motives of the new style of scientific investigation that developed so rapidly in the forty years from 1660 to 1700 appear to have resided less in its pragmatic implications than in the sheer inspiration of intellectual discovery, powered by that great discovery of method which ever since has proved so potent—the back-and-forth play between deduction and experiment—in Bronowski's powerful characterization, "fact and thought helping one another." Indeed, at its beginning the new science was actually able to contribute relatively little of real consequence to technology. And as the Newtonian revolution expanded, so also did the concept of a science pursued for its own sake, independent and quite different in its motivations from practical technology. This basic approach, which the early scientific societies, despite the orientation which some of them professed, actually did much to foster, was clearly congenial to the liberal climate of the time. It was, indeed, a liberal concept in the deepest sense. This is a point which we shall have occasion to recall later in the context of the significance of science in communist states.

It is also clear that the scientific revolution was, at the beginning, quite independent of industrial developments in the European countries where it occurred. Nowhere is this independence of the scientific from the industrial revolution better demonstrated than in the panorama of those same pioneering scientific societies of Europe, and especially of Great Britain. If, for instance, the dates of founding of a representative sample of the early scientific societies of Europe be tabulated, beginning with the Italian Accademia dei Lincei in 1609 and ending with the Manchester Philosophical Society in England in the 1780's, a curious pattern emerges. The first five of these societies, ending with the British Royal Society and the French Academy of Sciences, both formally established in 1662, were founded within an interval of about half a century. The second group, somewhat different in character, shows a similarly compact distribution in the dates of founding of its members. The British Royal Society of Arts and Manufactures was constituted in 1754. The Lunar Society of Birmingham, picturesquely named for its club rule of calling meetings on nights when the moon was full so that its members might find their several ways homeward over the atrocious roads, was established some time before 1770. The Manchester Philosophical Society appeared in the 1780's. All the societies in this group arose within a span of about thirty years. Yet a century elapsed between the dates of founding of the first group and the second. The industrial revolution was roughly coeval with the second group of founding dates. All of the earlier societies, therefore, appeared before it, and the initial stages of scientific development which they fostered went forward in its absence. It is of special interest in considering the circumstances and needs of the new nations in the field of science that the Newtonian revolution took place in a largely pre-industrial society.

And it was not only the careers of a few great individual scientific explorers that were lived independently of an industrial environment. The major steps in the transformation of world view in British society as a whole from an essentially Ptolemaic concept of the universe to a Newtonian one came, in the main, during that feverish period between 1660 and 1700—approximately eighty years before the start of the great period of British industrial growth. And it is hard, at this remove, to fully comprehend how consuming was its effect on society as a whole. Not only did the outlook of an entire nation during no more than forty years suddenly undergo a transformation more profound than any that wars or drastic political changes might have wrought. Even more prodigiously—and in the context of the new nations perhaps even more significantly—the fever and the excitement of the change were truly universal in the society, reaching far out beyond its rare leaders of Newtonian stamp. This astonishing movement opened windows for the intellect onto vistas so universal and compelling that in less than a generation the vision of a whole people was intellectually transformed.

Of such stuff was the scientific revolution made in its original setting. That setting, of course, may never be repeated today. It may be that a revolution of such intensity and scope can never sweep over a new society again. One must never forget the long centuries of special experience that underlay that historic and heady time. And yet many of its parameters are clearly relevant to the circumstances of more than one new nation in the world today. Familiar as all of them are with long and universally established technologies, some of the new countries have until recently been little more affected by the currents of contemporary world science than the European nations had been at the time of the original scientific revolution, and the intellectual and spiritual impact of the scientific climate could quite conceivably have an equally fresh and stirring and compelling quality for them today. The gaps of understanding that may exist between the arenas of science and technology in many new nations, moreover, and the further gaps between an infant science and a virtually nonexistent industrial structure, are matched by the similar discrepancies that faced the early European men of science. It is by no means impossible to imagine that in another guise a scientific revolution could be repeated in much of its earlier intensity and dynamism in some national and social settings which today are in certain ways comparable to that of Western Europe in the middle of the seventeenth century.

This has been a long digression into history. It was undertaken only because it may have a real bearing on this central question of the needs of the new nations for a living science. And it bears too upon one of the most important aspects of our role in bringing scientific and technical aid to the new nations—the understanding, at least in some measure, of the tremendous and fascinating complex of conditions which "spark" a scientific revolution. This question we may explore briefly before turning to the next general consideration—American foreign policy and the forces of science and technology in those nations of the world for which the scientific revolution has been an inherited tradition.

ʊʊʊ

MANY factors point to the need of the new nations for a science of their own. The first, the most practical, and perhaps the least fundamental is that, as the whole history of the scientific revolution has demonstrated so vividly, technology cannot remain a vital and a growing thing in the modern world without continuing nourishment from the wellsprings of a living science. Without a living, indigenous science a new country must depend heavily and indefinitely upon constant borrowing if its growing technology is not to stagnate. And such permanent dependence upon borrowed technology can be politically as well as technically and economically dangerous for a new country. For if the management and development of the technologies that it borrows tax its resources of understanding and innovation too heavily, technical dependence can easily lead and reinforce dependence in the economic and political spheres as well. The Soviet policy which has been so noteworthy in the past of pushing production machinery vigorously in its programs of technical aid to the new countries, thus permanently "entwining" Russian technology with the industrial development of a emerging nation, is instructive here. Furthermore, since no country can understand so well the subtle requirements and the new opportunities for technology within its own lands as the peoples who actually employ it and must live with its consequences, the effective adaptation of technology to local use requires, in the most pragmatic sense, both a living and a practical native science. It is no overstatement that, in the long run, a nation can be reckoned truly strong and independent only if it possesses both a vital technology and a vital science in appropriate balance.

In a different vein, the ability to make independent, original contributions to the world's store of scientific knowledge has come to be a mark of progressiveness, and even of successful national identity, in the modern world. How true this is has many times been demonstrated in Western Europe. Some technically and scientifically advanced nations have in recent years found themselves in positions with respect to some of the very new research fields where it would clearly have been more immediately economical to live on a technology borrowed from outside—a technology often enough developed elsewhere from scientific advances for which they themselves were originally responsible.

Consider in this connection British science and technology and the field of the organic chemistry of polymers and the physics of semiconductors. Polythene was invented in Great Britain, nylon in the United States. Transistors are an American contribution. Today the technologies of both fields are well known and everywhere available at the relatively modest cost of royalties. But the very practical opportunity of living on them indefinitely at moderate expense has not diminished British activity in theoretical research in polymer chemistry or in the physics of the solid state. It is a characteristic judgment of technically advanced nations that to follow the easy and apparently frugal course of continued technical borrowing as a substitute for original research is to sacrifice elements of national morale, national self-respect, and, in the long run, national autonomy far more precious than the price to be paid for them. The emerging nations, and indeed we ourselves, will be wise to take careful note of such experiences and decisions.

But these are all rather shallow reasons. Deeper ones follow upon some of the historical considerations earlier outlined. Without some structure of indigenous, living science the new nations are likely to have great difficulty in developing standards of judgment by which to apprehend the whole scientific "style" of the natural world. The instinct of what is credible and what is not, that fine sense of the scientifically genuine and the scientifically deceptive, require continuing direct experience for their perfection. Without the capacity for making such judgments a new nation must remain in a position where, in a practical sense, it will be highly vulnerable in its contacts with the outer world. It will be vulnerable, indeed, even in its acceptance of technical aid proffered in the most disinterested spirit.

Yet the greater danger is internal. For without such a sense of the world's scientific "style" informed judgments cannot be made domestically in a whole field of critical matters. It was not idly that the Reverend Solomon Caulker, the Vice-Principal of Furah Bay University College in Sierra Leone whose tragic death after the Rehovoth Conference in 1960 was an incomparable loss to Africa and to the world, remarked during the Conference "What we want from science is not prestige projects but the answers to our own witch doctors."

But it is upon the qualities of science as a structure of communication, of philosophy, of faith, that the deepest reasons rest. Without a living science, the new countries will be denied the cultural world fraternity that the fabric of scientific understanding implies. They will be largely excluded from that particular array of lofty concepts that is the priceless heritage of the scientifically literate peoples of the globe. In the world which they enter late as nations, the new countries stand in sore need of independent standards to which they may repair. Without a living science one of the most fundamental, as well as one of the most practical and accessible, of all standards will be denied them. Without it, they cannot well enter at a scientific level into those international combinations which, in addition to all the practical benefits that they bring, can be so important in commanding the belief and the confidence and the loyalties of peoples, especially in smaller political units, and in evoking their verve and their creativeness, in cultural and scientific fields no less than in those more immediately oriented to politics and power. We shall later return to this same point of the importance of building viable political combinations of sufficient size and to the place of scientific concerns in cementing them in yet another context—that of the international role of science for the nations of Western Europe.

Finally, and yet more deeply, an original science demands, as it also stimulates, those critical and creative habits of mind so essential to the new nations in every field—the unfettered, flexible, empirical view so essential to their growth and indeed to their very survival as independent states, and still all too rare among them.

$$\mathscr{SSS}$$

CAN the new nations in fact enter upon scientific revolutions of their own? If so, what will be their character? In one sense, the new nations should have a marked advantage over the nations of Western Europe in, say, 1800. They take the stage at a time when the basis of scientific, as of technical, knowledge is obviously immeasurably richer and more varied than ever before. To that extent we can expect their revolutions, if successful, to be even swifter than earlier ones, and the course to scientific maturity possibly shorter. An interesting and significant relation recently detected by scientific historians is that, if the rate of growth of the volume of the scientific effort be measured by several different and partly independent criteria for Western Europe, the United States, and Soviet Russia, it is found in each case to follow an exponential curve. But while the slope of this curve indicates roughly a doubling of the scientific effort every fifteen years in Western Europe, the corresponding figure for the United States is about ten years and for the Soviet Union about seven years, or possibly less. This is consistent with the successively later entries of the three nations in a major way upon the scientific scene. It is possible that a similar relation between lateness of scientific and technical maturity and subsequent rapidity of development could obtain for some of the new nations which only now are seriously preparing to meet the scientific standards of the world. But for these new nations the hazards, also, will be greater. The countries from which the curves of scientific growth have been taken are all socially and culturally highly developed. They are all extremely wealthy by the standards of the less developed nations, and they are all politically powerful. They are all populous, and large in geographic extent. Criteria which are valid for such states may not apply to smaller and weaker ones in isolation, regardless of how similar some other factors may be. The new nations are faced with the formidable difficulty of achieving an autonomous, competitively viable scientific effort in a world where the range of large-scale, versatile science is already immense and the scientific competition correspondingly severe.

To this major challenge are added a number of practical hazards inherent in their special situations, including the difficulties of securing training for original scientific work for more than a very few in a capital- and university-scarce economy and the difficulties of retaining those trained few at home, relatively isolated in a climate of popular opinion which at the outset may view the scientific way with hostility and will certainly do so with incomprehension. The establishment of adequate means to train and implement even a small core of qualified scientific workers in an isolated new nation is likely to require penetrating vision and extremely vigorous effort sustained over a long time.

There is much, however, that we can do in detail to assist here, through channels and by means already moderately familiar to us, and to some extent already in use. They include aid in the overseas training of research workers, and, probably more significantly, aid in the establishment of local institutes for scientific training. They include the various patterns of contractual arrangements already evolved, and others which can be and are being conceived between educational institutions in the new nations and various American universities of special competence in appropriate areas of scientific knowledge and skills. They include the many possible systems by which outstanding American teachers, administrators, scholars, research scientists, can represent us in the new nations—matters presently under extensive exploration in the President's Scientific Advisory Committee, the National Science Foundation, and elsewhere within the government. They include all the ways in which American scientific societies of eminence, notably the National Academy of Sciences and the American Association for the Advancement of Science, can aid in the establishment and encouragement of corresponding scientific organizations in the new nations. It would be hard indeed to overestimate the importance of such associations as enclaves of pioneering at the beginning of a scientific revolution— a role which, as we have seen, they played most importantly in the early stages of the scientific revolution in Western Europe, as also in both Imperial and Soviet Russia, and presently perhaps in Communist China.

In similar vein, a most important aspect of the scientific revolution in its earlier stages is the social value attached to scientific eminence. Such social valuation can be a powerful spur to progress in the early stages of scientific development in a country if it is accurately related to real as opposed to spurious or trivial scientific distinction. Countries newly experiencing scientific revolutions are not always prepared, however, to make such discriminations accurately. Appropriate recognition of real scientific merit as it develops in the new countries accorded in the scientific councils of more advanced lands can wield important and salutary influence—an influence which the British Royal Society, for example, has long and skillfully exercised.

In thinking generally about these matters, one is impressed over and over again by the concept of a "critical size"—and this in contexts other than the explosive mass of an atomic bomb. It is clear, for instance, that for a scientific research group to be stable, to be continuingly creative in its ideas and effective in their execution—in a word, to be successful—its membership must exceed a minimum number. This is not a large number, to be sure. It is not a very definite number, and no doubt it varies considerably with the character of both group and effort. But it is a number. The same may well be true of societies which are going through, or are about to enter, a scientific revolution. It may well be that some of the new nations are below this critical threshold—not only in wealth and in facilities for education and research, not only in economic or industrial level, not only in technology, but in sheer numbers of existing trained scientific talent, and in sheer magnitude of population from which such talent can in future be drawn. So special emphasis should be laid on the assistance that we may bring in helping to consolidate natural regions in a scientific and technical context which may include more than a single nation.

One of the most effective of all the "conventional" channels of scientific aid open to us may well lie in the establishment of such cross-national programs and the founding of cross-national cooperative training centers among the new countries. The establishment of local institutes on a regional basis, for example, designed to train students from more than one neighboring state at established university centers, returning them afterwards to the countries of their origin, in the general pattern which Israel has suggested in the context of various new nations of Asia and Africa, seems of special promise. Such institutes for training and for research, indeed, may do more than merely provide, temporarily, a "critical size." They could also become important factors in conditioning such neighboring new nations with inherently similar interests to work with common scientific aims, mitigating those damaging bonds of competitive national pride which at their worst can seriously impede or even fatally hamper scientific efforts undertaken wholly autonomously.

§§§

Now all this is excellent. Indeed, it is critically important. And yet, in a way, it represents simply an extension, an elaboration, of a pattern which we already know, making more ingenious, more comprehensive, and it is to be hoped more effective, a valuable but after all a basically conventional framework of thought and action. We need it badly. But we also need something larger and more original.

In the last analysis, we shall need a far deeper understanding than we now possess of the whole nature of a scientific revolution in a society newly awakened to scientific values. In no other or easier way can we attain to the real wisdom required to render genuinely significant and lasting assistance. It is true that in its details a scientific revolution must differ in each period that it occurs, and with each nation where it takes place. Yet there are certain important characteristics that are likely to be common to them all, characteristics which earlier scientific revolutions vividly illustrate, and which we shall surely do well to bear in mind.

The most significant, perhaps, is the truly cataclysmic nature of scientific revolutions in general. Though it is very evident that scientific revolutions can be long in the making and that they are typically initiated by the efforts and accomplishments of a gifted and dynamic few, the final period when the change affects a whole society—the span of its supreme significance—is characteristically amazingly short. In the west it was not the theories of Copernicus or the observations of Galileo or the reasoning of Francis Bacon that constituted the general revolution, critical though they were in igniting it. It was, rather, the years following Newton—the years, indeed, of the British Restoration—when the visions that had earlier compelled the pioneers, and the broader implications of the newer ideas and especially of their syntheses, suddenly infected a much wider public. It is worth emphasizing again in this context a point which has been earlier made. It is hard indeed at this distance of time to fully appreciate the incandescence of the Newtonian revolution when it captured the imagination of a whole people. Some of the new countries may well stand today on the similar threshold of another scientific revolution of their own, built around such recent intellectual concepts as those of probability and chance and new ideas of the nature of living matter.

When such revolutions culminate, their cataclysmic effects range to levels deeper than those touched merely by the explosive speed of change. Internally, the seismic social shifts which they entail must affect a nation profoundly, rending the generations, separating father from son in what may amount to completely different worlds, gravely threatening that precious margin of redundancy upon which societies in general—and traditional societies most of all—depend so heavily for their coherence and their inner vitality.

During such critical periods the new nations will be at their most vulnerable, in their external relationships as well as in their internal health. Then above all other times they will have to protect themselves vigilantly against subtle as much as against overt destruction or domination. It will not always be easy for them to do this effectively. In many cases the critical apprehensions in scientific matters, which only the experience of having lived with and through and having survived and profited by a scientific revolution can really provide, will not be adequately developed—and this just when they are most needed to implement wise decisions at the multifarious choice-points which the revolution will inevitably impose. Yet the courses chosen at such times of profound upheaval may well have fundamental and lasting significance, and the consequences of wrong choices will not be easily undone. And should such a scientific revolution itself fail at the critical point, widely held expectations are bound to be dashed. In the bitter disillusionment which must follow, political attitudes too may be dangerously affected.

At no stage in its development will a new nation need advice and wisdom more—wisdom to enable it to pass through the crucial periods of maximum change as rapidly as possible, wisdom to handle itself as effectively as may be during the trying time. Two of the deepest and the most urgent questions that we can ask ourselves in the whole context of scientific aid to the new nations may be: "Will we be prepared with such wisdom when and where it is needed?" and "Will we be prepared to lend it with real effectiveness and at the right time to any new country facing the trials of this transition when such a country may truly wish to share it with us?" Such questions are among the most poignant that we can ask in terms of common humanity. They are also among the most vital in terms of the very survival of the free world. For it is worth remembering a recent vivid and prescient characterization of the Soviet state as "the scavenger of the transition."

We probably have to answer these questions by saying that we are indeed very poorly prepared at present. Yet the assistance that we might provide through effective analysis and understanding alone, if it were truly far-seeing and genuinely relevant, could be more critical to new nations at such junctures of their history than any material aid that we could bring them in the context of science or than any specific measures to forward their scientific progress that we could devise.

In the final analysis, we probably know far less about the real nature of scientific revolutions than we do of the nature of the economic and industrial revolutions with which they are likely to be associated. Like those movements, it is clear that scientific revolutions are enormously complex and that they rest upon a multitude of prerequisite social and material conditions, many of which, surely, cannot be apparent at the present level of our understanding. There is far more to the nature of scientific revolutions than the substance of the science they embody.

Perhaps there is no more significant means by which the United States could become prepared, over the long term, to render scientific aid to the new nations of the world at a deeper and more meaningful level than we have hitherto been able to do than by the constitution of one or more advisory groups, perhaps formally outside of government but in constant and close touch with it and responsive to its needs, dedicated to a continuing major effort to understand scientific revolutions as social phenomena and to give policy counsel concerning them. Such a group, or groups, should include representatives of many disciplines relating to those multifarious facets of social change of which a scientific revolution is but one aspect.

Such groups, moreover, should be prepared for long-continued work. The efforts to understand must be sympathetic and persistent. It is reasonable to expect that advice of this kind will continue to be urgently needed for a long time to come, as new nations successively approach the thresholds of their scientific revolutions, and as the store of experience in the advisory groups themselves accumulates and acuity of analysis and judgment improves, as the deeper common denominators are sifted from more detailed aspects.

From the very nature of the task, an enterprise of this kind does not present an easy prospect. The disciplines and viewpoints which must be included and comprehended are so varied and divergent that communication itself will not be easy within such advisory bodies, and can only be developed gradually. At the best, years may be required to show substantial accomplishment. Yet we are not without models around which such undertakings could be built, as in the atmosphere, for instance, of the great university centers dedicated to international affairs.

Moreover, a beginning which could prove of great importance was made officially in 1960 with the establishment of a Research Advisory Committee to the International Cooperation Administration and to the successor Agency for International Development (AID), constituted under the chairmanship of Dr. Walsh McDermott with a Congressional appropriation of $6,000,000. Two years later the Committee assumed an important role in the United Nations Conference on the Application of Science and Technology for the Benefit of the Less Developed Areas, convened at Geneva as a much enlarged and elaborated successor to the earlier Rehovoth Conference. Acting as a Public Advisory Board to the Secretary of State, the AID Committee mobilized such a large and important group of American contributors that no question was left as to the depth of United States interest in the problems nor of the initiative of our country in attempting to meet them.

But the basic task which the times require is, of course, much broader and deeper than this, and in its very essence must be of much longer duration. It is also challenging and troublesome for reasons quite beyond those posed by the inherent nature of the task. In a purely practical sense, the popular climate in which such a group as the AID Committee must work is inevitably difficult. It is bound to be one where understanding of the vital character of its task for American as well as for world interests is persistently difficult to convey. Neither within the Department of State nor in the Congress nor in the nation at large have considerations of the relationships of science and technology to world affairs been traditionally dominant. Though these considerations are becoming notably more serious today, they still do not come easily or naturally. And effective work of such a body as the AID Committee critically requires sympathy and comprehension in such matters, widely shared within both executive and legislative arms of government.

To address a larger context, however, it cannot be emphasized too strongly that if such a general objective were truly achieved over the coming years, in whatever fashion and by whatever means, both we and the new nations could well feel that a major element had been added to our resources. Not only could it bring a better comprehension of the operation of presently little-understood social forces centering about scientific and technical change, the consequences of which must dramatically affect the whole configuration of world power in the years ahead; it could very conceivably provide aid to the emerging countries at the most practically significant of all levels as well. Never in world history, indeed, can such understanding have been more important than it now is and will continue to be in the age before us, an age of which not only space exploration but a comprehension of scientific and technical phenomena on a far deeper and wider scale than ever before, and a new order in their control, will inevitably be the symbols.

II. BEYOND THE SCIENTIFIC REVOLUTION

4
THE
"INTERMEDIATE"
NATIONS

W E MAY now turn to that second group of nations defined in the arbitrary classification suggested in the Introduction, comprising those societies whose own historical experience has directly comprehended the scientific revolution. They form a group which varies widely in other aspects of the life and being of a state—in population, in area, in wealth, in level of economic, technical, and industrial development, in geographic position. In scientific and technical sophistication they range from some states which have had long, continuous, and intimate cultural and often political associations with Great Britain, extending back to the years with her original fashioning of both the scientific and the industrial revolutions, to such a nation as Pakistan, whose own scientific revolution, is nonetheless genuine and deep, though recent, and though carried forward autonomously since political independence finds its essential roots in more remote colonial experience. In some ways this appears to be a highly artificial class of states. And yet the experience of a scientific revolution in the life of a society seems so profound as to make it a distinguishing parameter.

In many respects the most interesting and the most critical phases of the scientific revolution are those currently being experienced by the nations at what might be called the "nearer" end of this spectrum. Such nations, located particularly in Eastern Europe, along the Mediterranean littoral, in the Near and Middle

East, on the Indian Peninsula, and in parts of Southeast Asia and South America, are already culturally integral parts of the modern world, with essentially modern views of the whole scientific "style" of the universe. Their economies, in general, are still modest, with a low *per capita* income. Their situations, however, are not, by and large, the highly critical ones of some of the new nations. A number indeed are on the threshold of sustained economic growth. They are likely to be still markedly "tight" in respect of technically trained personnel, but in most cases patterns of training at the secondary level are established, and movements to strengthen them further are often evident. The pool of already skilled persons may be large enough, or almost large enough, to be autonomous, both for training new cadres and for undertaking fairly ambitious developments. Our technical aid to these countries must be particularly sensitively appraised. For it is desirable that every possible effort be made to stimulate autonomy, supplying only such overt assistance in the *adaptation and use* of technical aid as helps to achieve this end in the most vigorous and effective manner.

Substantively, the range of relevant technical help is not dissimilar to that for the little-developed countries, but it will naturally be somewhat broader in scope. The technologies of food production and disease control will still be of primary importance. But such technologies as those of geophysics, mineral prospecting and assay, soil prospecting and assay, the basic techniques of ore and petroleum processing, water planning and water use, the planning and use of other renewable resources, the development and uses of new materials, the exploration and development of new sources of power, architecture, and urban planning, will all be relevant. The deficiencies in this class of nations are likely to be represented not so much in a lack of sophisticated appreciation of technology—an appreciation which may, indeed, be highly developed—as in scarcity of trained manpower, insufficient or only marginally sufficient development capital, and a small and relatively lowly organized industrial structure. Perhaps more needed than anything else are the knowledge and skills of organization—the means to link technology effectively to an infant industrial structure on the one hand and to an infant science on the other.

These circumstances suggest at once some special avenues of technical aid open to us which may be particularly useful for the "middle" countries. They surely include wider provisions than we have made at present for the overseas training of their technical personnel, especially in institutes and industries in this country, and particularly aid in setting up technological training centers in the countries themselves, once again with special emphasis laid on centers designed to serve more than one country in a given region. We should bear in mind especially the crucial need for training in the techniques of the organization and use of technical knowledge and for establishing the facilities to put such training into effect. The opportunities, mentioned earlier in the context of the new nations, for American industrial firms with branches located overseas deliberately to aid in the technical education of the country by training a somewhat larger corps of personnel than they estimate will be permanently required for their own staff can be of special significance to the "middle" nations of the world.

One of the most exciting things about that revolution in the development and use of technology on the edge of which so many of the developing societies are poised today is the flexibility and originality for which its very newness provides scope. As an interesting case in point, consider the objectives of the current (and second) Pakistan Five-Year Plan, spanning the years 1960–65. It aims at an annual investment in technology of 10 to 15 per cent of the national income, with 3 to 4 per cent in foreign exchange coming from the advanced countries as long-term loans or gifts. It visualizes the establishment of an indigenous heavy industry, especially in the area of steel manufacture, where an annual output of 400,000 tons is projected. It aims at the local manufacture of fertilizers to replace present imports, thus implementing some of the features of Indian agricultural planning earlier referred to. Finally, and perhaps most significant, it envisions an extensive training program, with a planned output, ultimately, of 70,000 technicians per year.

Undoubtedly not all of these goals will be reached. But they are impressive in an Asian nation whose very official existence spans less than twenty years. And there is no doubting the verve and dynamism that can characterize such developments, once fairly begun. They have been vividly illustrated in Pakistan over the last years in the dynamic growth of both universities and government-supported technical organizations.

A particularly interesting example of the rate of growth of government institutions for technology in Pakistan in recent years is provided by the Council of Scientific and Industrial Research (C.S.I.R.). Conceived in the general pattern of the British Department of Scientific and Industrial Research, and established as an autonomous body in 1953 by the Ministry of Industries, this organization, headed by a distinguished biochemist originally of the University of Aligarh, a decade ago consisted of the Director and a very few assistants housed in small Quonset huts set in the blowing sands of the Desert of Sind, outside Karachi. Today the Council is a sizable national resource, with laboratories in Karachi, Lahore, Peshawar, and Dacca, and represents the largest aggregate of technical talent in the country. Work is in progress on a permanent Central Laboratories establishment in Karachi.

Four government Research Councils now exist in Pakistan in addition to the C.S.I.R. They include an Atomic Energy Research Council with a laboratory at Karachi and plans for the establishment of research centers elsewhere, an Agricultural Research Council, recently reorganized, a Medical Research Council, and a Council for Engineering and Works. Somewhat more than a year ago, moreover, a National Science Council was established, composed of the chairmen of each of the specialized Councils, together with a Chief Scientific Adviser to the President, Chief Scientists of the Ministry of Defense, two representatives from an Inter-University Board and each Ministry, and three scientists nominated by the President. Thus far and thus dynamically has government organization for technical work progressed within the first two decades of the life of a nation of "intermediate" class.

This year Indonesia is planning like developments, looking toward the establishment of an extensive group of government-operated scientific and technical laboratories of basically similar function, conceived perhaps most nearly in the general pattern of the dynamic Australian Council for Scientific and Industrial Research Organization, and reporting, again, at Cabinet level through a Minister of Science. The Government of Thailand in 1963 passed an Act of Parliament establishing an Applied Scientific Research Corporation as a principal agency for carrying on research in agriculture, industry, and health. It has profited greatly from Australian advice and counsel.

But progress in this area is still, as would be expected, most uneven among the intermediate nations. Thus Turkey today is still on the far side of the threshold of such developments of government support for science and technology, and needs them badly. It may acquire them fairly soon, however, in accord with legislation drafted and submitted for the creation of a Scientific and Technical Research Council.

It is particularly in the area of science itself, however, that the group of the "middle" nations may be at the most exciting stage of development. Since the scientific view of the world is well established in virtually all of them and for many represents a long inheritance, they characteristically possess a scientific "elite," holding sophisticated views and not seldom distinguished both in training and mature accomplishment. The heritage of independent universities is common to them all, and is, for the most part, of long standing. Turkey, for example, though at a quite primitive stage in respect of government support for technology and science, possesses four established universities and is presently building two new ones, at Erzurum and Izmir. The University of Djakarta in Indonesia has a long and distinguished history. And in Pakistan not only are there the older universities, like those of Lahore and of Dacca, inherited from an earlier political period, but since partition three new ones, those of

Karachi, Peshawar, and Rajshahi, have come into being. In them, as with their predecessors, departments and faculties of science have developed greatly over the last decade, while schools, colleges, technical training centers, and polytechnic institutions have multiplied apace.

The ranks of the scientific elite, however, are often distressingly thin in the "middle" countries, and they are in constant peril of being thinned further by systematic losses of their best members to more industrially advanced nations, in the absence of suitable opportunities at home. Because of this paucity of numbers, moreover, the members of this scientific elite in a dynamically developing "middle" country are likely to be cruelly overloaded both in the volume and the diversity of their obligations, and this represents a special danger.

Though there is likely still to be considerable mass indifference to the acquisition of scientific learning in those countries, there may also be a notable respect for it. Possibly because of the sparse distribution of highly trained persons in the population as a whole, there may be an especial regard for *individual* learning and a strong focus upon individual attainment, primarily in the context of individual benefit and individual merit rather than in that of the society at large. There are many obvious weaknesses, of course, in such a structure of values. One consequence that may not be immediately obvious is that in science, as also in technology, concepts and skills relating to the *organization* of knowledge itself are apt to be fairly rudimentary. A fascinating feature of this group of nations, indeed, is that among those of its members still in a preindustrial or an early industrial stage there seems more than a possibility that preconditions for a scientific revolution may exist resembling in some significant features those of Great Britain in the period, say, of the founding of the Royal Society.

If such speculations reflect even a part of reality, they suggest some relevant areas of scientific aid for the "intermediate" countries. Roughly, such areas can be referred to two categories: aid in the means of *obtaining and developing* new knowledge, and aid in the *organization* of that knowledge. The first category, as always, involves primarily the problem of the nature and means of higher education at home and abroad, and is most importantly a matter of university structure. The ratio of students to educational staff in the "middle" nations may range at least to twenty-five per instructor—a high figure for advanced training. There is a clear need for this ratio to be lowered as soon and as much as resources of money and of trained manpower will allow. Again, scientific training at the universities tends, naturally enough, still to be organized along essentially preindustrial lines, frequently providing insufficient opportunity for numbers of potential excellent research workers and teachers, especially in the lower academic ranks. The correction of this situation is, by its very nature, an excessively complex and difficult problem. All the aid which the advanced nations can provide here, particularly in the tactics and the logistics, as it were, of scientific training for industrial economies, will be greatly needed.

Problems of technical and scientific education, indeed, may be more severe in the "middle" nations than they are in many of the new countries. On the one hand such countries are beset with all the problems of educational poverty with which the new nations struggle; on the other, in many cases the "intermediate" nations stand in great need of educational reforms of a kind also indicated in some of the nations of Western Europe. Those that are beginning to industrialize are further plagued by woeful deficiencies in the effective use of existing scientific talent in their budding industries—and even by a widespread lack of sophistication in recognizing the indispensable role of properly trained scientific and technical talent to successful industrial development—just when they are most desperately in need of such development if they are to achieve their coveted and proper stature in the world. Since we have already briefly considered problems of this character for the new nations and shall return to them in the next chapter in the context of Western Europe, nothing further of them need be said specifically at present.

The area of training in the organization of knowledge is an

especially fascinating one. Here facilities for communication—in the strictly physical sense, in the sense of opportunities for personal scientific intercourse, in the sense of the constant exchange of information via books, periodicals, frequent and extensive scientific meetings—are critical. And all too often, for a variety of reasons, such facilities are still elementary. In our advanced scientific civilization we may easily forget that so apparently simple and yet actually so revolutionary an innovation as the scientific paper was made in our own society only about two hundred years ago. Without that seemingly elementary yet singular device which has done so much to make the knowledge of science cumulative, the scientific revolution itself might well have taken quite a different form—if, indeed, it could have occurred at all. Too many of the "middle" nations are still on the far side of such watersheds in the organization of knowledge—watersheds which we ourselves are far from having finally crossed today.

An interesting and suggestive experiment in bringing aid in this area has recently been inaugurated with respect to the nations of the Central Treaty Organization. Rather early in the existence of CENTO a Nuclear Training Center was established at Baghdad to serve the member nations. It was later moved to Teheran, and a Scientific Council for CENTO was organized, with a principal responsibility for administering and operating it. In 1961 the terms of reference of this Council were expanded to include all the phases of science within the CENTO area, and, with this broadening of concept, the United States entered the Scientific Council as a full member. Since then, several scientific conferences have been sponsored by the Council among the member nations on such subjects as science itself, science organization, and science teaching, as well as a survey of the state of science in the member countries by delegates from the United States, all bringing notable practical contributions to the forwarding of scientific communication and the organization of scientific knowledge. This last-mentioned Mission Survey, conducted in February and March of 1963, has pointed to several already existing institutes in various technical and scientific fields which could readily be made the basis for further cooperation in training and research among the CENTO nations.

There are few more versatile or effective social institutions in the nascent stages of the organization of scientific knowledge than the scientific society. The importance of its role in providing an enclave and a communications center in the early phases of a scientific revolution has already been stressed. But it can do much more than this. It can also serve as an arbiter of standards, as a maker and conserver of prestige, as a fountainhead of proper rewards. It has already been emphasized how desirable it is that scientific societies in the new nations be officially recognized by the corresponding bodies in more advanced countries, and that free interchange be established and constantly encouraged between them. In the present context, this matter may take on even greater significance. There is a large role and task here for our national scientific societies, and it is one to which, happily, they have begun in recent years to address themselves aggressively. A vivid example of this was offered a few years ago by the tremendous stimulus which was obviously brought to the new scientific associations of Pakistan—to the Pakistan National Academy of Sciences, itself a very new organization, and the Pakistan Association for the Advancement of Science—as its contacts with the scientific societies of the United States were advanced and consolidated. Today we see similarly growing relationships, with similarly stimulating effects, between the new scientific organizations of a number of other nations at roughly the same levels of scientific development and those of our own country.

§§§

IN LEAVING this arena of the "middle" nations, it may be worthwhile to recapitulate briefly some of the more important avenues open to us for assisting their scientific growth. Aid in structuring their educational systems to meet the scientific and technical

challenges of a modern industrial world is clearly of first importance. So also is aid in developing the fundamental techniques of
organizing and communicating scientific knowledge. Aid in establishing training centers indigenously and abroad, with special
attention given to regional centers, and aid in evolving well-
adapted curricula for them are evidently of equal import. The
avenues of assistance available in the supplying of appropriate
"scientific emissaries" to the new countries in the form of exchange research scholars and visiting lecturers of our own who
are of scientific distinction; further aid in the provision for visits
here of key scientific personnel of the "middle" nations; aid in
fellowship training; and last, but not least, aid at the level of
government sponsorship in the holding and facilitating of international scientific meetings in this country—an area where we
have traditionally been woefully weak—are not to be neglected.
It must be stressed once again how cardinally important it will
be to do all that we can to assist the establishment and the growth
of scientific societies in the "middle" countries, and thereafter to
maintain the maximum possible communication between them
and corresponding scientific bodies in our own country.

Finally and perhaps most important of all, it is vital to the
"middle" nations that they recognize the stature of science and
technology in their national economies, that they accord appropriate public recognition and status to their trained professional
talent in those fields, that they strive to the utmost to use them in
the most efficient manner, and that they widen both the personal
and the professional opportunities of these citizens to the greatest
possible degree. Closely connected with this is the importance of
an adequate appreciation by the administrative groups in the
"middle" nations, both public and private, of the vital role that
scientific and technical talent must play in industrial development. In all these areas, we can do much to encourage the "middle" nations, and to impress upon them how vital such strictures
are in the context of continuing health and growth of their science
and technology.

With this all-too-brief consideration, the extent of which does

scant justice either to the importance or the complexity of the
subject, we leave the new and the intermediate countries of the
world. The remainder of these pages will be concerned primarily
with the scientific scene in Western Europe, in Russia, and in
China. With the single exception of China, these are all nations
of such sophisticated industrial and technical status that it becomes very difficult any longer to distinguish arbitrary boundaries
in the close-knit, almost seamless fabric of what might be called
"scientifico-technology" through which the advanced nations live.
So there will be little to say in this context about technology
per se, and little distinction can longer be made between, as it
were, science "pure" and science "applied."

So far, too, the concerns which we have explored have had a
pronouncedly academic flavor, because such academic questions
underlie so very deeply all that happens in our changing scientific
and technical world. And nowhere is this more true than among
the new and the "middle" nations. Now, however, other factors
will appear, and accordingly, the emphasis of primary concern
inevitably will shift somewhat. Though problems of scientific
training must still claim prominent attention, in speaking of the
nations of Western Europe, and of the U.S.S.R. and China, we
shall obviously also be concerned with questions bearing more
pointedly upon the overt power structure of the world, in our
own time and in the more immediate future.

5

WESTERN SCIENCE
AND THE
IRON CURTAIN

In this seventh year of the space age, it is already hard to recall with the vividness that its significance warrants that day of August 6, 1961, when Major Gherman Stepanovitch Titov circled the earth seventeen and one-half times, traveling at 18,000 miles an hour in an elliptical course which took him at minimum altitude some 111 miles into the stratosphere and at maximum about 160 miles. For twenty-five hours and eighteen minutes he voyaged in regions until then unfathomed, and endured a prolonged state of weightlessness hitherto known only as a relatively fleeting experience to a handful of men in all of human history. When Titov finally ejected himself from his four-and-one-half ton vehicle and parachuted to earth he had set a high mark in exploration for his time.

That mark, of course, was soon to be surpassed, and most spectacularly by the Russians themselves. Since the flight of Vostok II have come the space voyages of the American astronauts, of Shepard and Grissom, of Glenn, Carpenter, Shirra, and Cooper, and of the Russians Nikolayev and Popovich. And finally, on June 14, 1963, came the most striking achievement of all in terms both of its spectacular quality and of the sheer endurance required for its achievement—the Russian "double" flight of Lieutenant Colonel Valery Bykovsky and Junior Lieutenant Valentina Tereshkova, the first woman to enter space.

But there were a number of things of particular interest about the flight of Vostok II, quite apart from the high human daring and the impressive ingenuity and power demanded for its accomplishment. One was its timing. A week later came the sealing of the border of East Berlin on August 13; twenty-five days later, on August 31, the Soviets announced their resumption of nuclear testing; twenty-six days later, on September 1, the conference of "nonaligned" nations convened in Belgrade. On that day also Major Titov, speaking to a large crowd of citizens in East Berlin on the Marx-Engels Platz, less than a mile from the border of West Berlin, pointedly remarked that the Soviet rockets that had propelled him into outer space could likewise deliver nuclear warheads to any part of the globe. Finally, as almost his last action before being closed into his space ship, Major Titov had dedicated his coming flight to the twenty-second Congress of the Communist Party projected for October.

Such coincidences underline with fresh immediacy the lessons already brought home by the history and the special character of Soviet space achievement since that day in October of 1957 when the first satellite was placed in orbit. They gave force to the observation that outstanding technical achievement can be extraordinarily powerful in cementing a people's solidarity, in augmenting its confidence, in reinforcing its pride, its verve, its sense of national identity. This is a lesson of special force and validity in the context of the science of Western Europe, and we shall return to it shortly in that connection.

At the same time, these coincidences also emphasize anew how closely and skillfully the Soviet knot may be drawn between impressive technical organization and accomplishment and initiative in exploration on the one hand and a grand design of power on the other. They demonstrate with special drama how effectively in Soviet hands a spectacular technology may be made to implement a many-sided psychological offensive, ranging from cajolery to indirect blackmail to direct threat, all added to and at the same time detracting from the genuine excitement and admiration which the sheer impressiveness of the feat alone should have inspired. The dispatches from London, Paris, Bonn,

New Delhi, Tokyo on the following day left no doubt that the event had been fully appreciated in its various significant aspects in the free world; those from East Germany, from Warsaw, from Prague, and the recurrent editorials in the press of mainland China made clear its tremendous immediate impact within the Soviet bloc.

At least two enduring messages were brought to the free world by the flight of Vostok II. Both were somewhat obscure at the time. Yet both were extremely important, and we shall return to them frequently in later pages. The first is underlined by contrasting the tremendous world reaction to Titov's achievement with that evoked by the latest and spectacular Soviet "double" space expedition. Technically, the latter was intrinsically a considerably more impressive accomplishment. It also included especially striking features which seemed well adapted to capture world imagination and to stimulate that mixture of fear and respect so often courted by the Soviet Union. Lieutenant Bykovsky circled the globe no less than 81 times, surpassing the record of Major Titov by a factor of nearly five. Though the partners in the dual course failed to rendezvous in space as was probably the original objective, the accuracy with which their movements were coordinated was itself an amazing feat. The flight featured the first woman astronaut—and one, apparently, only slightly trained at that. The efforts of the Soviet Union to capitalize on all these features were surely as intensive and thorough as in the case of Vostok II. Yet in spite of all its striking features, there seems little doubt that the world impact of this latest space achievement was pale in comparison with that of the earlier one. Nothing could illustrate more forcibly how indispensable is novelty in this sort of propaganda, and how rapidly the overwhelming impact on world opinion that the Soviets sought and at first so successfully won can decay, regardless of technical prowess. This is an important dimension for us to keep in mind in our own programs concerned with spectacular space undertakings, especially those involving the planned landing of men on the moon. It will be especially important to bear continually in mind the natural transistoriness of human attention as we weigh the gains from such programs against their cost in both human and material terms. We shall return to this point later.

The second lesson that was posed dramatically by the flight of Major Titov and its attendant circumstances, and that has been brought home with even greater force by all the subsequent history of Soviet technology, emphasizes how absolutely vital will be the continuing health and effectiveness of the community of Western Europe in scientific and technical matters over the coming decades as conditions of free world survival. In the last year this lesson has become particularly pointed with the notable general erosion of the concept of Western European solidarity. Our concerns about this dangerous development must be as serious on the scientific and technical as on the military, economic, and political sides. For while all the events of the last years pose a continuing challenge, first and indispensably, to research vigor and research quality *within* each nation of Western Europe, ultimately that challenge may be even more to the combined and coordinated capacity and to the confidence and spirit and sense of capability that such capacity can bring within the European Economic Community as a whole. Regardless of the current feeling in the Community about its own cohesiveness, and regardless of the energy and will of each nation, it is abundantly clear that no member of the European Community alone, over the coming years, can muster the technical strength or command the scientific universality independently to meet the imperative demands of the times.

The matter, indeed, goes far beyond mere substance; even far beyond the material capacity and versatility required for a strong and unified European science and technology. It goes to the very heart of the European concept itself. For it also involves those vastly important matters of loyalty, confidence, belief in a political sense which were earlier emphasized in connection with the new nations. For coming generations, the enduring greatest genius of Jean Monnet may well appear as his prescient knowledge that in the modern world there is a practical minimum of size, of strength, of cohesion in operating units. Above that minimum, citizens can find true meaning in their societies, can bring to them their best in loyalty and talent, can securely identify themselves. Below it, regardless of devotion and intent, such identification may be very difficult. In this context a closely coordinated technology, a closely woven scientific effort among the nations of Western Europe can well provide a powerful tie to reinforce economic and political bonds in the winning of functional unity. It may be persuasively argued, indeed, that nowhere is the charge to the free world likely to be heavier or more important than in its combined science and technology.

Appeals by various highly placed European officials for a consolidation of some major Western European technological concerns within the structure of NATO, accompanied by the evolution of a program of coordinated research and development and by the establishment of an agency empowered to contract for research and development projects throughout the NATO area, take on special interest in this connection. An important focus of such coordination and institutional reinforcement within the organization, with its thirteen European members, has been provided in recent years by the Science Committee of NATO and the office of the Science Advisor. Currently the North Atlantic Council of NATO, with its Science Committee, is empowered to award substantial grants for scientific research in the member nations. The Committee and the office of the Science Advisor, in fact, can act—and indeed are acting—in effect as an international science foundation. It is estimated that by the end of 1963 the fellowship program of the Committee will have totaled some $2.5 million. Further, the Committee is supporting summer sessions dealing with advanced scientific topics in European universities on a significant scale. Thus NATO Advanced Study Institutes have in recent years expanded the pioneering work of the summer schools at Los Houches and Varenna. In addition, grants are being provided for international study and research. In 1959 and 1960 nearly six hundred students were enrolled for study in countries foreign to them.

The Organization for Economic Cooperation and Development (O.E.C.D.), growing from the older Organization for European Economic Cooperation, has, with its daughter organization the European Productivity, done much to stimulate interest among all the nations of Western Europe in building adequate structures for industrial research. Eighteen states from Western Europe, together with the United States and Canada, are members of this comity. It has two scientific committees, one concerned primarily with research, the other with problems of scientific and technical personnel. Each has evolved quite extensive programs and plans. They include studies of scientific curricula in the schools and the introduction of newer educational methods in technology and science, the provision of continuing information to the member states respecting research and development expenditures, and studies of the relation between research investment and economic development. The O.E.C.D. is also directly concerned with the organization of cooperative applied research programs among its member states.

Attached to the O.E.C.D., the European Nuclear Energy Agency was established to promote cooperative development among member states in the field of the peaceful uses of atomic energy. A number of joint enterprises in research and development in this area have been undertaken under its auspices, including the Eurochemic Company at Mol in Belgium, involved with the reprocessing of nuclear fuels, the Norwegian heavy water boiling reactor project, now in operation at Halden for more than four years, and the Dragon High Temperature Reactor project at Winfrith Heath in England, with an initial budget of £13.1 million for a five-year program. Each of these undertakings is jointly financed by the various countries directly concerned. They have boards of management consisting of two members from each of the participating nations and operate under the general supervision of the parent agency.

Another international European agency which is deeply concerned with the development of atomic energy is Euratom, a creation of "the Six," with objectives similar to those of the

Nuclear Energy Agency of O.E.C.D. Euratom, with a staff of almost two thousand persons, is primarily a research and development organization. It operates a Joint Nuclear Research Center with branches in Belgium, the Netherlands, Germany, and Italy and has a substantial program of research contracts. Its work overlaps, and is coordinated with, that of the Nuclear Agency in many areas. Thus a substantial fraction of its budget (placed at about £30 million per year in the current five-year estimate) will be expended in support of projects already operating under the Agency—the Mol plant, the Norwegian heavy-water boiling reactor, the Dragon Reactor at Winfrith—as well as substantial additional undertakings.

In absolute magnitude, such developments are still on the whole modest by the standards of this country and of the U.S.S.R. But they represent a rapidly growing, if still often incoherent, nucleus for coordinated research and technology in Western Europe. Once a consistent philosophy has been developed for them, once they have been organized in a more orderly pattern than they presently are, once a concerted effort has been made to eliminate waste and duplication, a great deal can conceivably be built upon them.

They will be greatly strengthened by the existence, and by the growth which may be reasonably expected, of various associated "working" structures of international science. Such, for instance, is the European Organization for Nuclear Research (CERN) in Geneva, with fourteen member nations, a most successful product of UNESCO. CERN is intensively concerned with research of a fundamental character on high energy particles, and with very active programs in theoretical physics. It has accomplished a most noteworthy program in engineering and building the massive modern tools of high-energy physics, including the construction of a 600 MeV synchro-cyclotron and of a 28 GeV proton synchrotron entirely comparable with the similar instrument at Brookhaven, which now leads the world. CERN's spectacular installation, of pioneering design, involved the work of cooperative teams from Germany, France, Italy, Sweden, Switzerland,

and the United States. Its construction was thought to be beyond the capacity of any but the most advanced countries.

Notable too in the context of collaborative effort is the European Space Research Organization, with headquarters in Paris, planned to operate laboratories in Delft and in Italy and Germany and a launching site in Sweden. Its budget is predicted to be in the neighborhood of £110 million over the first eight years. Complementary to it is the European Launching Development Organization, concerned especially with the engineering of rocket vehicles for satellites, with an estimated budget of £70 million in the first five years. Interesting also in this context is the Training Center for Experimental Aeronautics in Belgium, which has made available to all the NATO nations equipment for research and facilities for education on a considerable scale.

Not to be forgotten either, especially for their wider implications, are the plans which have been proposed over the past few years for international universities in Western Europe. Such a project is that for a European University at Florence, generated by studies in Euratom, which has been under extensive consideration by the Community of the Six. Yet more striking is the proposal for a North Atlantic Institute of Science and Technology, conceived as an international scientific university comparable in scope and quality and organization with the best technical universities in the United States. It was drawn up and put forward by a committee sponsored jointly by NATO and by the Ford Foundation. These suggestions represent ambitious, long-term, and inherently difficult undertakings. Yet to be significant they need not reach such impressive goals as those originally envisioned. If administered so as to avoid conflicts with important national interests, if designed to strengthen the best national programs in education and to train students to return to their own countries at the end of their terms of residence, and if the necessity to terminate the ventures if they do not seem promising after reasonable trial is constantly borne in mind, then such institutions operated on a much smaller scale could fulfill very important functions.

Fundamental to any such plans for international education, and, indeed, underlying the whole vigor and effectiveness of coordinated international structures of European science and technology in general, are two basic requirements for science at the national level. The first inheres in the quality and the extent of scientific training in each nation. The second involves the general effectiveness of the support of science by the individual governments of the various countries.

At the level of national scientific education there is much to do, and some of it is reminiscent of the needs of less developed countries. In many Western European nations, programs of scientific education are of strikingly high quality in a substantive sense. But some are still inadequate to the requirements of modern competitive technology. In certain advanced European states there is still a serious shortage of qualified teachers of science, especially at the secondary level. In some countries there are specific conditions of unbalance which could with profit be remedied. In France, for example, a high proportion of gifted students enter the national schools of engineering because of the attractive careers to which such training leads and graduate thence into engineering positions, where their talents may permanently be lost to science. In the Netherlands and in Italy it may fairly be said that professiorial salaries are too low. The West Germany system of education nourishes outstanding individuals, but may still make inadequate provision for team research.

In the last ten years, the output of trained scientists and engineers in many countries has expanded by 25 to 50 per cent. This apparently promising increase, however, is actually quite insufficient for the conditions of the modern world. The annual rate for the production of engineers, tallied without reference to quality, is about 200 per million of population in the United States. The Soviet Union produces about twice as many, taken again without specific reference to individual quality. But the output of the European Economic Community has in the past averaged only about 70 per million per year—a figure that is far too low.

A part of the answer to these deficiencies—though clearly only a part—is economic. Both Great Britain and the United States invest about two per cent of their gross national product in the fields of science and technology, broadly defined, and devote about a tenth of this to what might be called fundamental research. France is not far from matching the two per cent level. Experience suggests that these are desirable goals if the human and material resources for scientific and technical education, research, and development are adequate to carry the necessary burden of advance.

The second great problem facing the nations of Western Europe in strengthening their science at the level of the individual state involves the formulation of coherent and effective national policies for its support within government, and the building of appropriate organizations to provide such support. Something has already been accomplished in evolving national policies designed to allocate human and material resources in science and technology so as to secure an optimum balance of effort within the country. More broadly, attention has also been given to making provision for systematic and continuing evaluations of scientific and technical matters in the total context of national polity. Debate on such issues, indeed, may currently be at its most dynamic. In many Western European countries it is still at a relatively early and unformed stage; in others it is much more advanced. But in virtually all there is lively exploration and argument, typified by the discussions that recently attended the establishment of the Advisory Council on Scientific Policy and the creation of the post of Minister for Science in Great Britain.

There has been considerable variation among the different nations in the precise forms assumed by governmental organizations for the support and conduct of science. But there are decided underlying similarities of evolutionary pattern. In most Western European governments the last years have witnessed fairly thoroughgoing reorganizations in administrative agencies charged with the execution of scientific policy. Such restructuring has in some cases resulted in the establishment of an operating group located within the upper reaches of government and charged with general responsibilities of coordination and execution. In other cases a single office has been created at ministerial level specifically committed to over-all jurisdiction in scientific matters. In many situations an organization or body of scientists has been officially constituted within government to provide high-level scientific advice on a continuing basis and to lend assistance in formulating policies and devising plans.

The timing of many of these developments in the nations of Western Europe suggests that they were greatly stimulated by events ushering in the nuclear and space ages. Thus in France a series of decrees were issued in 1958 establishing a new Inter-ministerial Committee of Scientific Research reporting to the Prime Minister, and appointing an advisory committee of twelve scientists. Within the governments of Great Britain, West Germany, Italy, and France the position of Minister for Science has recently been created. In Sweden and Belgium Science Policy Councils have been established under the chairmanship of the Prime Minister. In Greece a Ministry of Coordination has been constituted.

𝄞𝄞𝄞

WHAT is the concern of United States foreign policy with these developments? Obviously, the strengthening of science and technology at every level in the nations of Western Europe—at the level of research and education in the universities, of research institutes, of applied technology in industry, of the organization and administration of science within government—is of intense pragmatic as well as of great humanitarian interest to our own country. For in our age scientific and technical health are at one with sound economic growth, and so with political vitality. Thus the evolution of a solid scientific structure in each of the European nations must herald a significant augmenting of individual strength. But effective international cooperation and integration in matters of science and technology among the Western European nations are of even more intense concern to us, among other reasons because they may be closely linked with developments of international economic integration that can be so important for the future. Modern large-scale industry, depending on elaborate and extremely costly technologies rooted in turn in massive and specialized scientific activity, requires resources for research and development which cannot compete on the world stage unless they exceed a high and constantly growing threshold of magnitude. A nationally fractionalized European effort cannot achieve the necessary volume, the necessary specialization, the necessary versatility of science and technology to permit sheer survival, let alone healthy growth, over the long term.

In a yet wider setting, we presently have, and must retain in the future, a keen concern with the international organization of scientific activities not only in a European but in a world frame. Community of scientific interest, the inherent vastness of scientific and technical undertakings in many modern fields, and the basically international character of the scientific effort itself, all emphasize the importance of this involvement on a very broad scale. Concerns of this kind have achieved considerable tangible expression in recent years, notably in the formation of the International Council of Scientific Unions, in the unusually successful and productive International Geophysical Year, and in the establishment of the International Geophysical Committee, which, with the assistance of more than sixty national committees and the World Meteorological Organization, is operating World Data Centers to process the results obtained during the Geophysical Year.

One of the most interesting and potentially significant of such international cooperative projects planned for the immediate future is the International Years of the Quiet Sun. This undertaking envisages a broad program of measurements and experiments similar to and complementary with those conducted during the IGY period of sunspot maximum, covering with similar thoroughness the period of sunspot minimum due in 1964 and 1965. Scientists from more than thirty-five nations have indicated their intention to participate in the program, which will include investigations in ionospheric physics, aurora and airglow, cosmic rays, meteorology, and geomagnetism, among other fields.

ঔঔঔ

WHAT can we bring to the picture of developing European scientific organization, in background and experience? What, in turn, can we learn from it? While Europe has been moving rapidly in response to the historic pressures of the last years, we have been experimenting too. In some respects we have had a decided advantage. At the outset, by and large, our forms of industrial organization were more modern, our technology was more extensive and more sophisticated, we had an industrial plant which had not been cruelly damaged by a debilitating World War, and, as perhaps our most outstanding asset, we were the beneficiaries of political and economic unity across the nation. It has been remarked with some force that trying to build a modern massive structure of coordinated science and technology in a politically divided Europe carries some of the difficulties that would face us if each of the American states were an independent sovereign nation.

But if these priceless advantages were ours, there were other areas where we had much to learn from Western Europe. For Europe is, after all, the cradle of the scientific revolution, and until recent years was stronger in the tradition of original and basic scientific investigation than were we. From our earliest days as a nation we had been dominated by our instinctive ingenuity in technological development, and as late as 1945 we were still content in good measure to exploit the resources of basic research available in Europe—a circumstance poignantly emphasized by Vannevar Bush in the debate over the creation of a National Science Foundation.

Moved by the same world pressures that stirred Europe after the war, we also undertook a vigorous movement toward improved organization for science within government. It was unprecedented in magnitude and significance in our own history and, since it began somewhat earlier than similar developments in Western Europe and for a time progressed faster, it had the effect of making us, at least temporarily, genuine pioneers in the field. The organization, the mode of operation, and the achievements of the Office of Scientific Research and Development (O.S.R.D.), which during World War II was responsible for almost the entire conduct of the national effort in war research outside of the military sphere and which reported directly to the President, represented indeed a pioneering accomplishment. With this beginning, and spurred, like the countries of Western Europe, by the developments and the challenges of the nuclear age, we took some long steps in the organization of scientific matters within government in the postwar years. Some of them have already been touched upon. We established an Atomic Energy Commission, which, rooted in the older Manhattan Project of the Army Corps of Engineers, drew much in both its structure and philosophy and its pattern of operation from the older O.S.R.D. In rapid succession came the National Science Foundation and, at the level of scientific advice within government, special scientific advisory boards or committees serving the Atomic Energy Commission and the defense agencies of the nation; that very special innovation in research service to the nation, the Rand Corporation; and finally, the President's Science Advisory Committee, established in the Office of Emergency Management, within the Executive Office of the President.

But in the United States it was Sputnik I that brought in its train, and clearly in part as a consequence of its stimulus, a series of innovations and improvements of special note in the organization of science within our government—probably the most important which had occurred in the postwar period. The President's Science Advisory Committee was strengthened and brought directly within the White House. The post of a Science Advisor to the President was created and shortly attained great stature and significance. A Federal Council of Science and Technology was established to better coordinate the burgeoning advisory and executory functions of science within government, and in 1962 an over-all Office of Science and Technology was created, charged with the function of maintaining a comprehensive view of scientific and technical activities at the national level, of formulating broad policy, and of making available to the Congress authoritative reports and comments in those areas. Vast is the increase in the scope and significance of the federal support of research which accompanied these developments, as illustrated, for example, by the National Science Foundation, and in the active conduct of research within the context of the federal government, as exemplified by programs within the Atomic Energy Commission, the National Institutes of Health, and the National Aeronautics and Space Administration—brought into being during this same period through a reorganization and a great expansion of the much older National Advisory Committee for Aeronautics.

In dollar terms as well as in physical volume the growth of federal support for research and development in those years has been nothing less than explosive. In 1963 an estimate of the projected expenditures of the federal government for the current fiscal year in support of science and technology reached the extraordinary figure of $12.3 billion—more than the total of all government funds expended in scientific enterprises to and through the Second World War.

All these developments have been of interest to and have had considerable relevance for the countries of Western Europe, and it is clear that in a number of areas our experience has been instructive. But urgent problems in the appreciation and the adequate use of science and technology at the federal level still remain with us. The flight of Major Titov and all the related spectacular events of the succeeding years, including the four later Vostok flights, undoubtedly have given and are giving them added public emphasis and, to a degree, have added to their innate complexity, already challenging enough. Further developments in the structure, the range of duties, the modes of work of the President's Science Advisory Committee have come apace. The position of the President's Science Advisor has undergone some redefining to maximize its scope and stability.

But further improvements in dealing with scientific and technical matters at the level of the executive departments of the federal government are surely needed. Some are already well on the way. The creation of the office of Director of Defense Research in the Department of Defense has brought into being a body concerned with science and technology in military service which, under the extremely able direction and vigorous conduct which has been its lot, has proved powerful and indispensable. The creation of the post of scientific advisor in the Department of the Interior is of considerable interest. Historically, the level of in-house advisory competence in the Department of State in scientific matters, despite many efforts, has on the whole been weak. The creation of the new Office of International Scientific Affairs in the State Department and the extent and character of the activity which it has been able to undertake since the arrival of its first director in September of 1962, however, are most encouraging. But challenges to adequate scientific advice are especially urgent and complex in the foreign aid agencies, as has been earlier emphasized, and here they are perhaps furthest from being satisfactorily met.

Outside the executive branch, problems of rendering appropriate and adequate counsel at high government levels are legion. It is becoming increasingly evident, for instance, that the Congress stands today—and will stand even more tomorrow—in the keenest need of scientific advice in its daily work on a wider and more consistent basis than is presently available.

The establishment of the Office of Science and Technology mentioned above, which through its director can make periodic reports to the Congress upon matters of scientific and technical policy of concern to it, signals one important advance in this direction. Another, quite as significant and possibly of even greater importance in the daily guidance of affairs, may become available through the recently rebuilt House Committee on Science and Astronautics. Under the leadership of its new chairman, Representative George P. Miller of California, this Committee was reorganized two years ago to provide the first group in the Congress considering from the vantage point of continuing scrutiny the broad questions of scientific policy confronting the nation. One of the interesting ideas of procedure set forth at the time of the reorganization was that of holding periodic "status-of-science" hearings, planned at least every two years, to keep the Committee up to date on where the nation stands in major matters of science and science education. Such hearings have already been held, involving reports on some widely variant subjects within this frame, and have proved of considerable interest. They may enable the Committee to act effectively as a general advisor to the Congress at large over a considerable range of scientific and technical fields. The reorganized Committee, indeed, has been conceived in some quarters as the Congressional counterpart of the Federal Council of Science and Technology in the executive branch, and it has organized a capable scientific advisory panel to aid it.

Beyond these specific questions of how appropriate advice in scientific and technical matters can best be furnished to the executive and the legislative branches of the government lies a yet deeper and more general group of problems, fundamental to all our concerns with a national science. They center about how best to conduct substantive research itself directly in the national service, inside and outside the government structure, with all the intricate and difficult questions of opportunity and salary for the individual, of staffing and procurement, of the special status of quasi-governmental and private research organizations, that are involved.

In all these areas, which are still so much the subject of conjecture and experiment for us, it is quite clear that we will have at least as much to learn as to teach, for years to come. And this is yet another reason why it will be exceedingly important in the future that we maintain a maximum of communication, a maximum of sharing the experience, mistakes, and triumphs, with Western Europe. This is an extraordinarily relevant concern for United States foreign policy.

In a similar pattern, though at a different level of substance, United States participation with the scientists and technologists of Europe in pioneering the engineering of their own great international projects must surely be of immense benefit both to them and to ourselves. Such joint undertakings as the building of the CERN proton accelerator, in which United States scientific and engineering talent participated with that of several Western European nations, have the highest value.

ՖՖՖ

THERE is a final, and an overwhelmingly important, element of scientific policy in which both we and the nations of Western Europe have much to gain from the pooling of mutual experience—though at the moment, because of special circumstances, it may be we who must take the longest steps and who must be especially sensitive to associated dangers. It is an element curiously inherent in that first message emphasized by the flight of Major Titov, mentioned at the beginning of this chapter. The challenge concerns a matter which is utterly vital for our own future scientific and technical health and welfare and for that of Europe as well, namely, the maintenance, in the face of all the pressures that we confront, of our flexibility, our freedom, in the development of our research resources—material, but most particularly, human. For there are few things more precious to us than our autonomy, our balance, our pluralism, in technology and science no less than in other aspects of our national being.

There could be no more fatal error, either for us or for Western

Europe, than to suppose that, because the Soviet Union has grown from the status of a less-developed society to a technically and scientifically vastly powerful state in an extraordinarily short time, the *operating patterns* by which this was accomplished have any special validity for ourselves, or that the national "sense" of the primary values of science and technology there are precisely like our own. To require that the most vital and enduring aspects of our own scientific effort *necessarily* have any immediate practical bearing upon affairs economic or military would be to deny one of our most precious avenues of growth—in fact, actually to negate one of our major spiritual forces. It takes strength and wisdom, in the face of the threats and challenges that beset us, to remember such cardinal truths.

In guarding the continuing autonomy, the continuing flexibility, the continuing plurality of our scientific forces, one of the most difficult kinds of policy questions must constantly be reiterated in the implementation of such major efforts as the expanded Project Apollo program initiated by the President in the spring of 1961, with its objective of putting a man on the moon by the close of the decade, for which an expenditure of approximately $3.6 billion is projected for the current fiscal year. Such a commitment appears truly major when reckoned, not so much in terms of the national income, but in the reserves of appropriately trained manpower available for total service to the nation. It may be no exaggeration, indeed, to predict that much of the basic strength and symmetry of our national scientific effort over the next few years will depend importantly upon how well the claims to money and manpower made by such vast but highly specialized undertakings can be balanced against those broader requirements of plural training and plural research so vital to the continuing scientific and technical growth and well-being of the country.

In our thinking about this particular vast project, moreover, in our evaluation of its proper claims against those of more diverse scientific and technical ventures that are competitive with it—and which must be competitive, since we have not the wealth in money or in men to do all things—it will be wise to bear continually in mind another relevant matter to which we have already referred—the demonstratedly ephemeral quality of the impression made on world opinion by spectacular Soviet space achievements. A serious and abiding question which we should recurrently ask ourselves might run: "In the final and critical view of the world, will it be spectacular space achievements, or outstanding success in bringing assistance on a penetratingly significant and relevant level to those countries which need it most acutely, that will make the most abiding impression and command the most lasting respect?"

The decisions which we make over the coming years in meeting such great questions, the ways in which we resolve such powerful dilemmas with which the world and our time confront us, will be watched with keen interest by the Western European nations. They will be vital for our own welfare, and, depending on how well they are taken, the experience that we achieve can be of high significance also to the entire free world.

So it is clear that there are abundant opportunities for effective American aid to the nations of Western Europe in their scientific and technical concerns, both individually and in combination, if it can be brought with that abiding sense of the sharp limitations of our own vision and capacity that the least modicum of wisdom compels. We must recognize fully that these limitations are quite as great in respect of the advanced nations of the world as they are in the context of the new states. But they are of a very different *kind*. A cardinal element in that wisdom will involve the continuing awareness that a true internationalism in science and technology among the industrial nations of the West must, in the end, mean far more than a mere coordination of research programs through international research bodies, far more even than the training of scientists at international universities or than their subsequent careers in international research centers and engineering establishments, important though these are. All these activities can only serve as the organizational expression—at best a superficial thing—of that internationalism at the level of substance which is so cardinal a quality of science.

Failures of communication among peoples inheriting a common tradition must perforce be reckoned as failures in the very processes of scientific understanding, and, at a yet deeper level, as failures in realizing an essential quality of scientific verity. So the final goal of cooperation among the nations of Western Europe must imply an interpenetration of research concerns at a profound level along the frontiers of substantive knowledge with which modern science is so deeply involved—visual and radio astronomy, high-energy physics, geology and geophysics, communication theory, the study of behaving systems in living things, of the mechanisms of heredity, of the differentiation and coordination of cells in the living body, and all the rest of those avenues of inquiry the compulsion of whose fascination far exceeds the confines of the most comprehensive formal organization. In many of these fields, the very instrumental tools of inquiry are beyond the financial and technical resources of most individual states; in all of them the intellectual demands far surpass the capacity of any one country to meet them individually.

The requirements and responsibilities which such considerations must place upon any people—and especially our own—presuming to aid in the strengthening of science and technology in Western Europe as a whole are immense. In no area of potential overseas assistance, not even that to the new nations, must scientific planning be more carefully meshed with educational, economic, and social considerations. Nowhere are humility and patience, persistence and a comprehensive and sensitive understanding more urgently required if, over the coming years, our assistance to Western Europe is to provide not merely a temporary stimulus but a significant and a lasting benefit.

6

SCIENCE AND THE
LIBERAL FRAME:
THE U.S.S.R. AND CHINA

THE FLIGHT of Major Titov on August 6, 1961, and all the following developments in Soviet space achievement, have yet another aspect of great interest. They underline with what intense practicality and particularized concentration the Soviet state can treat its technology and its science. Such a massive concentration of effort on a specialized and conspicuous technology, like that of rocket boosters of great power, undertaken in a thoroughly practical manner, has a familiar ring in the annals of Russian technical development. The earlier history of Russian aeronautics, for example, through those first decades after Tupolev and Zhukovsky joined forces in 1918 to launch the Central Aerodynamics Research Institute and the Zhukovsky Air Academy and to initiate consistent development programs in the field of military aircraft gives vivid evidence of how much an extraordinary ability to keep continually abreast of technical developments in other countries, to adapt them effectively and dynamically to specific ends, to plan over long periods with enormous endurance, tenacity, and singleness of purpose may accomplish, and how much, on occasion, it may compensate for an uneven program of research, or a neglect of highly plural, experimental technical approaches.

Do such examples imply a general lack, within the Soviet Union, of research attitudes and research procedures comparable to our own? Such a query may be expanded further. Perhaps its general content can best be condensed in two specific but highly hypothetical questions. The first part of the first question might run: "Since the scientific revolution was so uniquely a product of the liberal enlightenment of seventeenth- and eighteenth-century Western Europe and was so closely entwined with it, does not the very structure of science embody, as an essential part of its nature, these same elements of liberalism?" Much of the evidence of history might incline an observer to answer this half of the question positively. Then follows the second half, almost the converse of the first: "Is science then likely to be a liberalizing element in any society of which it is a part?" Here again I believe the answer to be positive and highly significant, though perhaps most relevant to the new nations.

This introduces the second query, on which we may well focus. "If these things are true, does it follow that a concept of scientific inquiry in its least pragmatic and purest investigative sense is likely to be disadvantaged in a totalitarian society by the extent to which it clashes with the dominantly pragmatic ethic; and, where such a science does emerge, is it not likely to encounter serious difficulty in developing a strength and range, and an over-all degree of quality, comparable to that of the western world?" And the final question, consequent upon this, may be: "Does this mean that in the Communist countries—and most notably in the U.S.S.R. and China—we may expect science as a whole to be retarded, and over the long run to find difficulty in competitively matching western achievements?" A clear answer to this last question, whether negative or positive, would obviously be of enormous interest. But it is not a simple question, and simple answers—and assumptions based upon such answers—can be both misleading and dangerous.

To be sure, there appears to be some evidence—and perhaps especially recent evidence—to suggest an affirmative judgment. Despite the brilliance of the technology of the Sputniks and the Vostoks, and despite the brilliance and the magnitude of many other recent Soviet engineering achievements, notably in the fields of mining and metallurgy and hydraulic engineering, there is some suggestion that Soviet science, taken as a whole and over a very broad front, may be of a less uniformly high standard than our own. Despite its tremendously impressive and still rapidly increasing volume, it seems in many ways less fine-textured and of a more uneven character. This has been the judgment of a number of acute recent observers, including at least one highly-qualified former scientific attaché in Moscow. It seems, indeed, to be a frank assessment of Khrushchev himself. To a remark by a United States scientific attaché that Americans would eventually pass the Soviets in their launching capabilities for space travel, Khrushchev is reported to have responded: "America is powerful and strong. If Americans put their mind to beating us, they can do it."

Recent changes in the Soviet Academy of Sciences, indeed, may have implied among other things a growing Soviet dissatisfaction with both their scientific and technical progress and its general orientation. They also underline two other aspects, both of very considerable interest. One is that familiar and overweeningly pragmatic orientation which typically accompanies the drive to impress science in its every aspect into the service of the military and political power of the state with the least possible delay so characteristic of Soviet administrative philosophy. The second is more subtle and speculative. It could be that this and other changes in the official structure of Soviet scientific administration signal a growing feeling on the part of Soviet planners at high governmental level that the period when Russia can rely heavily upon borrowed research and technology to power her further development may be drawing to a close—that henceforward Soviet technology must be based to a much greater extent on Russian research, domestically undertaken.

The rather sudden retirement of Alexander Nesmeyanov after a decade of service as President of the Soviet Academy of Sciences, which took place at an extraordinary general meeting of the Academy on May 19, 1961, and his replacement by Mstislav Keldysh, appears to have been correlated, among other things, with a new Kremlin program to concentrate the structure of research in the service of special technology and to accelerate further the conversion of research results into practical application. It is interesting indeed in this context that one of the criticisms leveled at the Academy under Nesmeyanov was that it dealt too much with theoretical and nonpractical problems. It is interesting, too, that Nesmeyanov himself at one time proposed a series of rather drastic changes in the patterns of scientific inquiry planned and conducted at the level of the Academy, designed to free that body from many of its applied functions and permitting it to concentrate more heavily on truly scientific research. This philosophy, contradicting as it did the long-standing Soviet dogma that theory and practice should everywhere be closely united, was forcefully expressed by Nesmeyanov in 1958, and again in 1960, the year before his retirement. It appears to have been held heretical in at least some politically powerful quarters.

Nesmeyanov's retirement was followed by a fairly extensive reorganization of the structure of the Academy, involving among other things what appears to be a tighter and more rigid specialization with respect to subject material, replacing the older departmental organization, under which research was directed along quite general lines in broad comprehensive fields, by much more narrowly focused divisions. To an inquiry made in May of this year by a member of a United States Delegation of the Atomic Energy Commission visiting the Soviet Union as to whether there was not a feeling that this reorganization in fact had the effect of bringing the older local scientific academies under quite strict and direct control by the National Academy and whether this might not involve a rigidification of structure which could adversely affect freedom of scientific inquiry with resultant damage to scientific progress in the U.S.S.R., Keldysh replied that he did not feel that control by, but only "consultation with," the National Academy was involved.

Perhaps even more striking evidence of these underlying themes in the current philosophy, organization, and operation of Soviet science, however, was offered just before the appointment of Keldysh by the creation of a new and comprehensive agency above the Academy in the administrative hierarchy, charged with the control of all the scientific work of the country as well as of all the international scientific contacts of the Soviet Union. This State Committee for the Coordination of Scientific Research, to which the Academy (formerly reporting directly to the Council of Ministers) is now responsible has the significant charge, among other things, of supervising the quickest possible introduction into the economy of the results of scientific and technical discoveries made in all Soviet governmental agencies. It is interesting that it was headed originally by Lieutenant General Mikhail V. Krunichev, former head of Soviet aircraft production, once Minister of Aircraft Industry of the U.S.S.R., Aviation Minister, and Deputy Chairman of the State Planning Committee. In this new assignment, Krunichev acted with the nearly pinnacle authority of Deputy Chairman of the Council of Ministers of the U.S.S.R. Thus for the first time the Soviet Union had established a truly comprehensive coordinating center for all research and development. Even more significantly, the responsibility for decisions involving scientific and technical development now was centered at the very apex of the Soviet power hierarchy—at the level, literally, of the Deputy to Khrushchev himself. Krunichev died of heart failure on June 2, 1961, to be succeeded by Konstantin Rudnev, but the system remained unchanged and Rudnev assumed the same authority as his predecessor.

It is hard for one accustomed to the modes of scientific organization and procedure with which we have grown up and which are standard in this country and in much of Western Europe to imagine that an organizational pattern of this sort could be the most stimulating for a creative national scientific effort. Further, it is interesting that not only Krunichev, but also Rudnev and Keldysh, come from distinguished backgrounds either in military science and engineering or in the administration of such activities—indeed, these are dominant themes in the biographies of all three. It may be a fair inference that these reorganizations, with the new directing personnel they have incorporated, will among other things result in an added drive to dedicate much of the research and technology of the country to applied military development. In this connection, a rather striking tribute to the pragmatism of a prevailing Soviet view of science was recently given by Alexander Topchiev, chief scientific secretary of the Academy of Sciences, in his definition of "basic research" for an American visitor. Basic research, he said, is that research in which the chances of "success" are less than fifty per cent—a view which could hardly be more sharply at variance with the Western concept of the aims and ideals of fundamental investigation.

All these things may hint that a widespread, plural, creative scientific effort in the Soviet Union could have difficulty, over the long run, in remaining competitive with that of the free world. This may very well be correct. And yet it is most dangerous to accept such a conclusion uncritically. In a purely practical sense, it is opposed by the characteristic Russian genius, displayed so often in the past, for planning purposefully and for pursuing clear objectives with an unparalleled single-mindedness, coupled with unusual skill and vigilance and effectiveness in keeping abreast of and successfully adapting research results obtained elsewhere in the world. How contemporary are both that genius and the facilities for implementing it is emphasized by the extraordinarily far-flung information-gathering and information-processing facilities of the Institute of Scientific and Technical Information, with its extensive establishment in Moscow. Even if the domestic research effort of the Soviet Union were over the long run to prove somewhat inferior in quality and depth, considered over its whole front, to that of freer competitors elsewhere, such pragmatic expertness can go far in practical terms toward compensating for other deficiencies. And it is not to be forgotten that in 1962 eight out of fifteen members of the Communist party presidium had technical backgrounds, as in 1959 did more than a third of the nearly 750 deputies in the Council of the Union of the Supreme Soviet and about the same percentage of the more than 1,200 delegates to the congress of the Soviet Communist party.

But there may be a profounder point to consider in this context.

Among the complex cross-currents which characterize Soviet science there appear again and again evidences of a genuine liberalism. Clearly it is partly a historical inheritance. Partly it is evidence, once again, that a body of science powered by creative workers is likely to cultivate strong elements of liberalism, whatever its official environment. Though the severity of the opposing political climate in which it works apparently fluctuates widely in time and place and with respect to the subject-matter particularly affected, much of Soviet science appears able to maintain at least a half-liberal cast despite the pressures to which it is subject. This tenaciously surviving—and possible tenaciously growing—strain of liberalism at the level of the working scientist is of most serious account, now and for the future.

For when all is said and done, there is an impressive body of scientific work in Russia, powered by some remarkable contributors. In such fields as oceanography and geophysics, inorganic and physical chemistry, crystallography, nuclear physics, and even areas of genetics and radiation biology, and in other fields as well, notable work is going forward. This body and tradition of sicence have deep historical roots. And yet, paradoxically, those roots are essentially alien in origin. Immediately, they represent an inheritance from Czarist Russia. But it is important to bear in mind that Imperial Russia in turn inherited both the corpus and the tradition directly from eighteenth-century Western Europe. However much Soviet science may have been distorted in some areas in recent years—most notoriously but by no means exclusively in the field of genetics—the best Russian science is essentially Western in form and content. It really dates only from the time of Peter the Great.

On his various trips to Western Europe and as a part of his general program for the westernization of Russia, Peter assembled a collection of European physical and chemical apparatus which he brought home and deposited in the Kuntskamara, a museum in St. Petersburg that became in effect the first demonstration laboratory in Russia. Late in his life Peter planned an Imperial Academy of Sciences, and it was organized by his successor

Catherine after his death in 1724. The plans for both the Berlin and the St. Petersburg Academies of Science were drawn by the great German mathematician Leibnitz. Swiss, French, and German scholars were invited to St. Petersburg, were made members of the Imperial Academy, and were asked to select and train Russian students. Among the Western scholars of high distinction who responded were two members of the great Bernouilli family and the Swiss Leonhard Euler, one of the most prolific mathematicians of all time. Euler's whole life, indeed, was spent as a member of the Berlin and the St. Petersburg Academies of Science. Thus the traditions of Western science dominated the form and structure of the Imperial Academy at its inception, the German tradition being especially strong. Western influence was equally important in the early Russian universities—in the University of Moscow, founded by Michael Lomonosov in 1755, and in the Universities of St. Petersburg, Kazan, and Kharkov.

Until 1917 postgraduate study in western European universities was considered an essential part of Russian scientific training. During that century and a half the broadly based Western science of Russia came to boast a considerable number of prominent names. Some, like the chemist Mendeleev or the psychologist Pavlov, are known to virtually every scientific scholar. The work of a greater number, like the zoologist and pathologist Mechnikov, is known to a more limited and specialized audience, but much of it has been genuinely pioneering and of high quality. In recent years this high tradition has been continued and expanded. Names like Kapitsa, Tamm, Fock, Landau, Kurchatov, Veksler, Kolmogorov, to mention but a few, stand very high in world scientific achievement. Nor have Nobel awards been strangers to recent Russian science. Nikolai N. Semenov, a vice-president of the Soviet Academy of Sciences during Nesmeyanov's presidency, won the Nobel Award in chemistry in 1956. By 1959 the Nobel prizes in physics and chemistry which had been awarded to Russian scientists since World War II had reached four, a quarter of the total for the United States and about a fifth of those awarded elsewhere. Interestingly—and probably significantly—

there had been no Russian awards in physiology and medicine, contrasting with no less than sixteen for the United States.

A science firmly established in these traditions cannot readily be destroyed or even fatally perverted, regardless of the regimentation to which it may have been or may be subjected. Peter the Great was probably as sensible as Khrushchev of the extent to which the pragmatic aspects of scientific development can be made to contribute to the technical might—and especially to the military might—of the state, and no doubt it was for those qualities that he primarily valued science. He may have been as little aware, or as little caring, as was Stalin of the aspects and values of science that are so vital to its long-term prosperity and of the requirements of science for a liberal climate of freedom. Such unawareness of these values or lack of concern for them, however, has not been characteristic of the creative Pasternaks of Russian science, whose ranks, over the generations, have been impressive and which continue to swell. Today, moreover, those ranks are in some senses more effectively implemented than ever before by a powerful system of domestic universities, by an extraordinary web of governmentally operated research institutes with massive facilities, and in addition by the copious inflow of carefully processed and effectively distributed research information from all over the rest of the world.

But at times the difficulties of these Pasternaks of science have clearly rivalled those of Pasternak himself. The whole history of Russian science, indeed, may in one of its dominant aspects be credibly described as a constant struggle between that spirit of free inquiry and the bonds imposed by the formidably pragmatic cast of the national philosophy and the narrowly dimensioned controls of its political and administrative systems. In some areas the struggle has clearly gone through serious crises at various times in recent years.

It is a very special tribute to the endurance so characteristic of the spirit of free inquiry in men that the struggle has surely remained at least a draw in many areas of science. In the absence of some serious unbalancing factor this ambivalent position, so resistant to precise analysis, could, and probably will, endure for a long time to come, and it is extraordinarily difficult to assess. It will clearly be affected, among other things, by the degree to which it is possible to establish significant cooperative scientific programs on matters of common interest between Russia and the West in the coming years. It is surely most important that such joint programs be encouraged to the greatest possible degree. There has been some progress in this area, even though it has been both sporadic and fraught with impediments. Thus the Russians were active participants in the work of the International Geophysical Year, though the extent of their collaboration was uneven, and they are currently continuing observers, and to some extent participants, in the work of CERN. In the future, continuing collaboration of this kind will surely be as important to Western science as to that of the Soviet Union, and it is to be hoped that openness of communication from both sides can be achieved and maintained, at least in limited areas.

But ambivalence makes the problem far from easy, and it is rendered more difficult by another kind of Soviet scientist who has figured especially prominently at international councils in recent years. In a curious way he thoroughly typifies the most sophisticated—and often the most thoroughly camouflaged—version of a purely pragmatic Soviet science. He speaks the language of science, he is frequently very well trained and may even be accomplished in his field. He is well aware of the liberal views of the scientific ethic held by his opposite numbers, and he is frequently extraordinarily adept at exploiting them. Characteristically he is personally charming. In effect, he is a Soviet scientific commissar. He is a type that, for a variety of reasons, we find most difficult to understand. We sometimes even find him difficult to recognize, or to admit if we do.

How prevalent is he among the legions of Russian scientific workers today? If, as seems likely, his is a specialized vocation for which he is particularly trained, how far are his attitudes and his basic philosophical orientation shared by the mass of Russian scientists? Or are most of them simply indifferent to such matters, confining their concerns to the political sanctuary of the labora-tory? And what of those Pasternaks of science, many of whom are older men, conspicuous in the past or in the present but trained in an earlier era? Are they still permitted flights of fancy? And are their ranks being augmented by equally gifted and imagina-tive recruits in significant numbers? Khrushchev's blazing words at his now famous conference in March of 1963, at which nearly a thousand artists and writers were left in no possible doubt of the dangerous degree to which they had offended the state by the unorthodoxy of their thought and expression, suggests how narrow the margin may still be in areas of creative thought. So also does the rather striking circumstance that since the death of the real Pasternak, a spiritual cult has grown around his memory, and his grave at Peredelkino, near Moscow, is reported to be the center of frequent and extensive gatherings of youthful followers to attest his memory. If similar circumstances apply widely in the context of science, the query may well be pertinent whether any science can truly thrive over the long term when its higher philosophy is consistently denied it.

Obviously, the whole picture of the position and the future of creative science in Russia is immensely complex, and sweeping predictions or categorical deductions are evidently both im-possible and dangerous. But the multifarious questions that at-tend it are of far more than academic interest, and they demand continuous exploration at a very deep level. Such exploration, like that of the nature of scientific revolutions in the new nations, will demand the coordination and the concerted focusing of many minds of many disciplines, extended over a long time to come.

ᔕᔕᔕ

WHEN we come to Chinese science, the picture is yet more fascinating and more enigmatic. No American scientist has visited China to witness its technology and its science at first hand since the regime of Mao came to power in 1949. From that time until 1958 there had probably been less than a score of visitors from Britain and even fewer from other of the free nations of Europe, and there had been virtually no formal and discerning accounts of Chinese science and technology. The bamboo curtain has been equally opaque from the other side. Communist China has resolutely declined invitations to join the International Council of Scientific Unions—because of the membership of Taiwan in that body—and scientist-representatives from the "Peoples' Republic" have been conspicuously absent at all the conferences sponsored by the Council and from related international contacts.

Despite this general paucity of "hard" information, however, some first-hand data of great relevance, as well as an extensive body of highly informed inference, has become available within the last five years. Particularly notable first-hand information was provided by a month's visit to mainland China made in 1958 by the Canadian geophysicist J. Tuzo Wilson. His accounts, published in several forms, provided the first real "window" on Chinese technology and science in a decade. Even more illuminating has been the recent visit of a delegation of six members of the Royal Society of Great Britain who on Chinese invitation spent a fortnight touring establishments in the northern part of the country. Their combined observations, together with data now available from many other sources, can lead to only one conclusion. However we may have hitherto regarded it, or however much we may have tended to ignore it, Chinese technology and Chinese science are impressive today, and they are rapidly becoming more so.

In an earlier chapter we noticed the ancient roots and the typical pioneering quality that characterized the growth of technology in prehistoric and in early historical China. It flowered at a period when the West was at a very primitive stage. With that flowering there came also notable developments in related pre-Newtonian science—in practical mathematics, in astronomy, in geology, among other fields. They are reminiscent of similar and often contemporaneous advances in Egypt, in the Middle East, in Greece. Some of these resemblances could well be more than coincidental. For modern archaeology has given a substantial hint that there may have been prolonged contacts between China and middle Asia along the ancient trade routes extending much further back in time than we had imagined, and with them a proliferation in both directions of technical and early scientific lore in times far more ancient than those of Marco Polo.

So there is a long tradition of skill and imagination and enterprise behind Chinese technology, and we should anticipate a capacity for rapid and aggressive technical development today. Yet in spite of this, the present attainments come as a marked surprise to the uninitiated. The pressures for expansion of technology on the Chinese mainland have been intense since 1949. In the peak production year of 1942 under the Nationalist régime, for example, coal production in China amounted to a little over sixty million metric tons. By 1957 that figure was reported to have exceeded 120 million tons, raising Communist China to fifth place in coal production in the world, following the United States, the Soviet Union, West Germany, and Great Britain.

Again, we have heard much of the extraordinary and bizarre compaign, during the height of the "Great Leap Forward" to induce peasants all over China to set up tiny and primitive furnaces for the smelting of iron ore. Such an unrealistic effort could only lead to failure on a massive scale, and this did occur. But that picturesque episode is all too likely to lead us to forget that China had reached sixth place in world steel production in 1960 when China operated at peak capacity, being only slightly behind Japan.

Geological workers are clearly being trained for mineral prospecting work on a massive scale in China today. Their numbers probably increased a hundredfold between 1949 and 1961. They are not all by any means well or comprehensively trained geologists. But they constitute a formidable army quite capable of scouting effectively for hitherto unsuspected reserves of mineral wealth. And this they have clearly been doing with success. Significant ore reserves of copper, nickel, lead, molybdenum, tungsten, aluminum, antimony, tin, among others, have been reported in recent years and may have been considerably exploited, often with substantial aid from the Soviet Union. At Paiyin in Kansu, in Anhwei, in Yünnan there are copper workings, and lead deposits are worked in Hunan, Yünnan, and Liaoning, from which important shipments of concentrates are known to have been made to the Soviet Union.

Production of electric power increased about sixfold beween 1952 and 1959, though even at the expanded figure consumption of electrical power represented only 60–70 kilowatt hours per capita, as contrasted with a consumption in the United States of nearly 4,300. True to ancient tradition, and responsive to the same exigencies of flood and drought and crop failure, great emphasis has been laid on the development of methods and facilities for weather prediction. It is reported that only the United States, Russia, and Canada now have more weather stations than mainland China. In the field of meteorology as a whole, moreover, China is said to have advanced in world standing from thirtieth to fifth place in the short span of twelve years.

These and many other examples which could be cited can leave no doubt of the impressive technological gains of which China has been and is capable—gains made possible in part by a centralization of such concerns in the research organizations of the industrial bureaus of government and the industries subordinate to them. In this connection it is of interest that neither the universities nor the institutes of the Chinese Academy of Science seem directly responsible, nor indeed are especially concerned, in this area.

Impressive as they are, such aggressive developments in technology do in fact represent the natural extensions of an older tradition. At bottom, they may be more expressive of energy and will than of striking originality. Like the technologies of nuclear power and nuclear weaponry, much of their substance could have been, and no doubt was, adopted from China's great mentor in the technology of the West, the Soviet Union. It is rather to Chinese science that one turns for an index of originality and a key to the longer future. And here too, as the recent visitors have left no doubt, the achievements have been remarkable in some areas.

It is interesting at the outset to note an important condition which at present must seriously limit the Chinese scientific effort and in the future could play an important role in determining its ultimate character. It is clear that the absolute numbers of scientists in mainland China who are fully qualified by long and intensive training is still quite small, and it is probable that an older core, trained in the West, is still influential. In mathematics, for example, it has been estimated that in 1961 there may have been fewer than four hundred researchers with training equivalent to the doctorate, and in all the natural sciences there may have been less than fifteen hundred workers at doctoral level currently engaged in research. Interestingly, this figure compares with another estimate of about two thousand for the number of Chinese receiving advanced degrees prior to 1949 who were still actually living on the mainland in 1961, and suggests that there may scarcely have been replacement of research workers at this level of training in the intervening period. Education at home to the level of the doctorate has clearly not yet involved large numbers. At least until very recently, of course, hundreds of students went to the Soviet Union for training—probably totaling in the neighborhood of seven thousand by the end of 1958. Some 1,200 to 1,500 had apparently completed graduate work in the U.S.S.R. by 1961 and returned to China.

But against this small current population of active workers with advanced degrees must be set the reported figure of entrants to the Chinese universities, which increased from approximately 35,000 in 1950–51 to an estimated 250,000 in 1959–60. Total university enrollment is believed to have grown from about 117,000 in 1950 to the neighborhood of 810,000 in 1960. Peking University, occupying a site which includes the grounds of the old Yenching University of Harvard University fame, has been radically reorganized in recent years and adapted especially to concentrate on training for research and teaching in the basic sciences. With a tenfold increase in its working laboratories from about 20 to approximately 200, with a calculated student quota of about 11,000, and with a firm basis of scientific training already established, it cannot fail to swell the ranks of trained scientists in China significantly in the next years. And Peking University is only one of an extensive university system undertaking similar, if less advanced and ambitious, campaigns at the present time.

Even assuming that the present comparative shortage of highly trained and competent scientists in China will compel the nation for some years to concentrate attention in limited areas, carefully chosen for their bearing upon the total national aspirations, it would be the greatest mistake to assume that this means that there have not already been some very impressive accomplishments, and that more may not be expected. This point was brought into especially sharp focus by the recent visit of the delegation of the Royal Society to Peking. It was reported that in solid state physics and electronics there was some very impressive work, and the estimate was made that within five years to a decade important new research contributions in these fields may be expected from China. Investigations at Peking in the fields of high polymers, in crystallography, and in metallurgy created much the same impression; and research in chemical fields, though somewhat behind this mark, was nevertheless well advanced. Programs were reported as very well directed, and the complexity of ideas involved was of an order with which British laboratories would have been dealing some years ago. About half the equipment seen was of Russian, East German, or Czech origin, but there was a significant amount from the United Kingdom, Japan and Denmark. More significantly, a good bit was of domestic origin, already being supplied by what may be a considerable indigenous electronics industry.

But there was an interesting obverse to this picture reported by members of the Royal Society delegation whose particular interests lay in the biological sciences. At the Peking Medical College, work was of a standard comparable to that of the 1930s in the West. But the development of research over the broad front of the biological sciences proved extremely uneven and seemed responsive to the individual interests of relatively few gifted workers in the field. Thus excellent work was reported in experimental embryology, apparently because of the presence of a handful of European-trained researchers in that field, but there was no entry, as yet, into molecular biology, though the Chinese biologists were well aware of the field. Most interesting in its broader social and political significance, a wide gap appeared to separate academic biology and agricultural practice. Such a divorce is so reminiscent of a pattern which at various times has isolated and impoverished agricultural practice and development in other Communist countries as to suggest that it may be significant in this context.

∽∽∽

So MUCH for a representative sample of current Chinese science at the substantive level in some of the enclaves where it has already achieved extraordinary progress, and established, clearly, a yet greater potential. What now of the broader aspects? What, if anything, can we conjecture with respect to future patterns of substantive growth, and future directions of philosophy?

There is much in these headlong developments to recall the forced-draft pattern of both technical and scientific development in the Russia of the early 1930s, though clearly China has had to start further back. Unlike the Soviet Union, China has virtually no long-established tradition of modern science. As we have noticed earlier, she stood almost completely outside the Newtonian scientific tradition until near the end of the last century. Even then, her contacts were of a far more limited and far more episodic kind than those of the Russia of Peter the Great. They were provided mainly by a relative handful of Chinese students trained abroad who had returned home, and by an even more limited influx of

European scientific immigrants. In contrast with her long and brilliant and virtually unbroken tradition of technological advance, it is probably safe to say that China entered on the postwar world devoid of any really rooted tradition derived from the original scientific revolution, with all that this implies of individual philosophy and social content. Except for a small—but probably influential—band of Western-trained scientists, largely working in some twenty-one research institutes of the Academica Sinica and the National Academy of Peking, there were few to comprehend, or even be aware of, the deeper implications of the scientific way when the Communists in 1949 took over half a continent. And in contrast to Soviet Russia, those who succeeded to power and have continued in it since can claim virtually no experience of science in their individual training or backgrounds, and are conspicuously alien to its subtler meanings. The slate, at the beginning, was indeed very nearly blank.

What was to be written on it, of course, was a ferociously keen official appreciation of the pragmatic values of a science applied to power, in the familiar pattern of much of Soviet official scientific philosophy and development. It was absolutely inevitable that the Communist Chinese should turn to the Soviets both for material help and, more lastingly, for their philosophy and methods of organization of a state science. That turning produced consequences so decisive for the present and so significant for the future that it will be worth-while to consider for a moment one or two facets of its history.

On January 25, 1956, Mao Tse-Tung announced at a meeting of the State Supreme Council that there should be a "long-range plan for the elimination of backwardness in the economic, scientific, and cultural fields." Thereupon the State Council, at the direction of the Central Committee of the Communist Party, established a Planning Committee for Scientific Development, headed by Marshal Ch'en Yi, Vice Premier and a member of the Politburo. The Committee was charged with drawing up a Twelve Year Science Plan, to run from 1956 to 1967. It is a special tribute to the intense importance which the government by then had attached to scientific development that this plan was assigned so long a term, unrivaled outside agricultural fields.

A draft was prepared over the next seven months by some two hundred Chinese, assisted by seventeen scientists from the U.S.S.R. It was presented to the Eighth Congress of the Chinese Communist Party in September and endorsed a year later. It then went to the Soviet Union for review by several hundred scientists. Shortly thereafter a delegation of over a hundred Chinese scientists discussed the Plan further in Moscow and reviewed its nearly seven hundred projects, in about one hundred of which Russian help and cooperation was solicited. This development seems to have signalled the final Chinese decision to expand their scientific base as rapidly as possible, and to do it quite literally in the Soviet pattern. There is evidence that in the single year 1955–56 the sums officially budgeted for scientific activity were increased sixfold, and by November 1957 over one hundred Soviet experts had come to work in Peking.

Though this was the culmination of what may well prove to be a final determination of the shape of governmental organization in Chinese science, the roots of the philosophy and action and of the Soviet influence which guided it are to be found at the very beginning of Mao's regime. Immediately after 1949, exhaustive inquiries were made by the government of China into the structure of the U.S.S.R. Academy of Sciences and particularly into its role in organizing and controlling science as a state enterprise. On the basis of those inquiries an Academica Sinica was created, taking its name but not its structure from the earlier Chinese Academy. Its first President, Mo-Jo, immediately visited the Soviet Union. It has been estimated that at that time there were perhaps ten thousand scientists in China holding academic degrees in the natural sciences, another ten thousand in agriculture, possibly twenty-five thousand in engineering, and some seven thousand in medicine and health. Of the approximately two hundred physical and natural scientists who in 1960 were members of the Department Committees of the Academy, nearly all were leaders in science or rising scientists prior to 1949. About

one hundred and fifty of them are known to have received training abroad, some eighty in the United States and the remainder
mainly in Europe and Japan. The composition of this core around
which domestic science was originally built and continues in
considerable measure to operate is important to bear in mind.
For, small and isolated as it was, it included among its members
a high proportion with direct experience of the traditions of
Newtonian science. And small though it was, and embedded in an
alien philosophical environment, its general influence must surely
have outweighed its numbers. How philosophically significant
that influence was or presently may be, or might become in the
future, is a key question the answer to which, at present, is
almost impossible to gauge.

From 1949 until 1956 the Academy functioned as the agency of
government charged with official responsibility for the national
administration of science. The 1957 reorganization, not wholly
unreminiscent of the one which was to come somewhat later in
the Soviet scene, brought an increasingly centralized control, and
one focused higher in the governmental hierarchy. It was a control vested with broad and comprehensive responsibilities in the
shaping of policy and equipped with very extensive powers to
enforce its decisions. Operating on the "principle of subservience
of scientific research to the requirements of the state" the Communist Party decreed that scientific research must henceforth be
conducted entirely according to plan, and not in response to the
personal interests of the scientists involved. In effect, this meant
that scientific policy planning headed directly to a member of the
Central Committee in the Party. In the Soviet Union, the similar
order of centralization was at least mitigated by the fact already
noted that a considerable proportion of the power elite in the
state, whatever their scientific philosophy, had at any rate come
from earlier backgrounds which included scientific or technical
training. In China, as we have noticed, this was not true. Senior
scientists typically had little or no association with Party officials
and little voice in the shaping of policy.

One purpose of this move was evidently directed precisely to the Soviet pattern of centralizing the control of science and its associated technology as a power asset for the state. But another motive, related and yet somewhat different, was undoubtedly the personal control of the scientists themselves, whose tendencies toward freedom of thought and expression were almost certainly considered to represent a significant danger to the government. This tribute to the influence of even a minuscule core of Western-oriented scientific tradition is worth bearing in mind.

It appears that most of the scientific research in China at present, outside of the universities, is conducted within the Academy. It has grown greatly, and essentially in the Soviet pattern of organization. Research institutes in specific subjects proliferated more than fivefold over the six years to 1958, with the total staff listed for that year standing at almost 30,000, including about 6,000 actively engaged in research. It is of course extremely difficult to judge the caliber of all the work in these institutes. Such a judgment, in fact, may not be particularly important. Undoubtedly the research is spotty in quality, dotted with peaks and dissected by valleys. Its immediate configuration is likely, at this stage, to result quite sensitively from the influence of relatively few dominant personalities. But it could change rapidly, and with equal sensitivity.

The importance of Soviet philosophy and Soviet help, through example and instruction and material aid, in the shaping of Chinese science is one of the most conspicuous features of the whole pattern. Not only have Soviet engineers and scientists been welcomed in numbers into China until very recently, not only have numerous Chinese scientists and engineers been trained in Moscow, but many collaborative scientific enterprises were initiated between the two nations, some of them of striking character. One of the most interesting involved the Russian collaborative scientific center at Dubna, originally conceived at the Lebedev Physics Institute. This center, located about one hundred miles north of Moscow on the Volga River, was set up originally in 1946, and ten years later was constituted a joint institute for research in nuclear physics, comparable in function to CERN, for the primary use of Soviet scientists and representatives of twelve other Socialist countries. One of its major efforts, evidently a response to developments in nuclear accelerators which the Russians were closely watching in the west, was the construction of a 10 bev proton synchrotron, planned at the time as the highest energy atom-smasher in the world and designed to give the Russians a commanding lead in the field. This instrument, however, turned out to be of seriously faulty design.

Chinese nuclear physicists were invited in numbers to Dubna and worked there so effectively that at the peak of collaboration in 1961 about a third of the scientific papers from the center bore the names of Chinese authors. At one point, moreover, China contributed about a fifth of the operating expenses of Dubna—three times that of any nation of the Soviet bloc itself. Again, in 1957 a major agreement was signed providing for Chinese cooperation with the Soviet Union on a variety of research projects over the five-year period from 1958 to 1962, including nuclear research and development. Moreover, the Russians provided the Chinese with a 10 megawatt research reactor at the Institute of Atomic Energy in Peking.

In view of this close association of Chinese scientific development with that of the Soviet at the levels of philosophy, training, material aid, and collaborative undertakings, it becomes of great interest to speculate what may be the immediate and the long-range effects of the current Sino-Soviet rift. The assistance agreement was abruptly canceled after only two years, and there seems little doubt that China's nuclear program was considerably crippled by this move, for she is already behind the schedule widely estimated in the West for her first detonation of a nuclear weapon. Resentment on this score, indeed, may be an important underlying element in the current feud. In this bewildering area of speculation the significant elements are so complex and the swift-changing panorama of facts so elusive and inaccessible that great care must be exercised in reaching conclusions at present. Especially should we be cautious about estimating the effects of this split on the rate of development of Chinese science and technology, particularly in the nuclear field.

In this connection two further points seem of some interest, merely as possible "tips of an iceberg" projecting through a sea of appalling ignorance. One is that although the Soviet Union undoubtedly made a generous contribution to Chinese nuclear development in furnishing a nuclear reactor to Peking which is capable of producing plutonium for atomic bombs, it appears, even at the outset, to have been one shrewdly measured in terms of weaponry. It was designed to utilize uranium fuel enriched to only two per cent, in contrast with some similar reactors furnished to nations of the Soviet bloc, which may utilize uranium enriched up to ten per cent. Furthermore, in the typical pattern of so much of Soviet foreign aid which was remarked earlier, this contribution seems to have involved "entwinement" with a Chinese dependence on supplies of fuel from the Soviet—supplies, of course, which are presumably cut off at present. Now it is hardly likely that these features went unnoticed by capable Chinese scientists at the time that the installation was made. It is hard to imagine that the gift was not received in much the same spirit of sophisticated calculation in which it was apparently made, with the Chinese looking on it merely as a valuable way-stage in the development of their own independent nuclear technology. In fact, they are thought at present to have at least four nuclear reactors.

The second point, carrying a like implication for that growing independence of Chinese science toward which the nation appears to be striving diligently and effectively, is that Russian scientists seemed conspicuous by their absence in Peking at the time of the visit of the Royal Society delegation in 1962, and no project leaders were interviewed who had been trained in the U.S.S.R. The impression left with the delegation was that, while the Chinese were both free and generous in acknowledging their debt to the Soviet Union, they regarded such assistance distinctly in the light of an initial send-off, and were bending all their energies toward achieving technical and scientific independence.

This impression was further heightened when, on September 25, 1963, China announced the establishment of a World Federation of Scientific Workers, dedicated to "the advancement of science in Asian, African, and Latin American countries." Among more than a thousand Chinese and foreign scientists reported to be in Peking for the occasion there were apparently none from the Soviet Union, and no reference was made to Sino-Soviet collaboration.

Dramatic as it seems today, it is entirely possible that the Sino-Soviet rift, even if it should prove as lengthy and as deep as present circumstances suggest, will have little permanent effect on either the rate of progress or the orientation of Chinese science and technology. Though both may suffer a considerable immediate setback, they are likely to emerge, ultimately, as yet more powerful elements in a nation scientifically, as politically, an astute student of Russian methods and patterns, but operationally independent of them.

The deeper question, of course, lies much farther in the future. It is essentially like the one posed earlier in the context of Soviet science. Communist China is a nation which in the eighteenth and the nineteenth centuries absorbed far less of the Western scientific tradition than did Imperial Russia. Even during the first half of the twentieth century its introduction lay principally with, and indeed was largely limited to, a scientific elite, brilliantly modern in outlook but in numbers only a minuscule drop in an overwhelming sea. Yet when Communism came, it was the members of that elite who formed the core for a reorganized Chinese science. Now they were asked to serve a science pragmatic in philosophy, officially dedicated to the furtherance of the power of the state, and administered by men who had absolutely no knowledge of or exposure to the Newtonian tradition.

Here is an ambivalence of viewpoint in which the extremes are far more widely separated than in the U.S.S.R., and probably of even greater intensity in the bitterness of their contrasts. If we speak of the Pasternaks of Russian science, we must also keep in mind the underlying explosiveness of conflicting philosophies which came briefly to the surface in the Chinese period of the Hundred Flowers.

The present rapid growth of Chinese technology and science may represent the beginning of a period in technical and scientific evolution which for Russia is nearly drawing to a close. It will surely be some time before China reaches the point where the greater part of her development must rest on a pioneering fringe of knowledge which she, in common with the rest of the world, must originate independently. There is still an enormous amount to be borrowed profitably, and while this remains true we may expect rapid and spectacular gains to continue even under totalitarian regimentation. But what will happen afterward? Can an original science continue to flower in that atmosphere? Or will the atmosphere itself be imperceptibly altered, in response to a growing recognition of the underlying requirements of a free science—a knowledge clearly held at present by a proportion at least of those senior scientists who are probably still important in the effort—or possibly in response to demonstrated failures under the existing conditions? Where will the ambivalences lead? On which side will they ultimately come down? These are fascinating and immensely important questions. At present, they are unanswerable in the context of this, the most enigmatic social evolution of our time. We can only remain ever watchful of its course, hoping for the ascendancy of liberal elements, hoping for a break in its isolation. And as we watch we must exercise every vigilance never to underestimate its potential and its power and remember always to keep our powder dry.

SUGGESTIONS
FOR FURTHER
READING

Atomic Energy in the Soviet Union. Trip Report of the United States Atomic Energy Delegation, May, 1963.

BARANSON, JACK. "National Programs for Science and Technology in Underdeveloped Areas," *Bulletin of the Atomic Scientists,* vol. 16, no. 5, May, 1960, pp. 151–155.

BLACKETT, P. M. S. "Planning for Science and Technology in Emerging Countries," *New Scientist,* vol. 17, no. 326, February 14, 1963, pp. 345–346.

———. "Science, Technology, and World Advancement," *Nature,* vol. 193, no. 4814, February 3, 1962, pp. 416–420.

COCKCROFT, SIR JOHN. "Investment in Science." Presidential Address Delivered to the British Association for the Advancement of Science at Manchester, August 29, 1962. *Nature,* vol. 195, no. 4844, September 1, 1962, pp. 875–880.

———. "Scientific Collaboration in Europe," *New Scientist,* vol. 17, no. 323, January 24, 1963, pp. 170–172.

FOUNDATION UNIVERSITAIRE. *Increasing the Effectiveness of Western Science.* Brussells: Author, 1960.

GOULD, SIDNEY H., Editor. *Sciences in Communist China.* A Symposium Presented at the New York Meeting of the American

Association for the Advancement of Science, December 26–27, 1960. Publication 68. Washington, D.C.: American Association for the Advancement of Science, 1961.

GRUBER, RUTH, Editor. *Science and the New Nations.* Papers presented at the Conference on Science in the Advancement of New States held at the Weizmann Institute of Science in Rehovoth, Israel, 1960. New York: Basic Books, Inc., 1961.

KAPLAN, NORMAN. "The Western European Scientific Establishment in Transition," *The American Behavioral Scientist,* December, 1962.

KISTIAKOWSKY, GEORGE B. "Science and Foreign Affairs," *Bulletin of the Atomic Scientists,* vol. 16, no. 4, April, 1960, pp. 114–116.

KRAMISH, ARNOLD. *The Peaceful Atom in Foreign Policy.* New York: Harper and Row, for the Council on Foreign Relations, 1963.

NATIONAL ACADEMY OF SCIENCES–NATIONAL RESEARCH COUNCIL. *Recommendations for Strengthening Science and Technology in Selected Areas South of the Sahara.* Prepared for the International Cooperation Administration. July 1, 1959.

Remarks by the Honorable Dean Rusk, Secretary of State, at the Centennial Celebration of the Massachusetts Institute of Technology, Cambridge, Massachusetts, Friday, April 7, 1961. Department of State Release No. 201, April 10, 1961.

SHONFIELD, ANDREW. *Attack on World Poverty.* New York: Random House, 1962.

STALEY, EUGENE. "Scientific Developments and Foreign Policy," *Bulletin of the Atomic Scientists,* vol. 16, no. 1, January, 1960, pp. 7–13.

Symposium on World Food and Population. Annual Meeting of the British Association for the Advancement of Science, Cardiff, Wales, September 5, 1960. See contributions by P.M.S. Blackett, D. V. Glass, W. Arthur Lewis, and Norman C. Wright.

U. S. SENATE. COMMITTEE ON AERONAUTICAL AND SPACE SCIENCES. *Soviet Space Programs: Organization, Plans, Goals, and International Implications.* Staff Report, 87th Cong., 2d Sess., Washington: G.P.O., 1962.

WADDINGTON, C. H. "Talking to Russian Biologists," *The Listener,* vol. 69, no. 1764, January 17, 1963, pp. 119–121.

WILSON, J. TUZO. *One Chinese Moon.* New York: Hill and Wang, Inc., 1959.

INDEX

Academica Sinica, 99–101
Academy of Sciences, U.S.S.R., 83–84, 99
Adams, John Quincy, 3, 4
Advisory Council on Scientific Policy, U.K., 69
African states, 7, 21, 30
Agriculture, 19–20, 57, 97, 99
Asia, food production, 19, 20
Atom, peaceful uses of, 23, 65–66
Atomic Energy Commission, U.S., 5, 73, 74
Atomic energy, in new and "intermediate" nations, 23
Atomic testing, 61
Atomic weapons, 4, 7–8, 40
Atoms for Peace, 23
Australian Council for Scientific and Industrial Research Organization, 53

Bacon, Francis, 42
Basic research: China, 96–97, 105; "intermediate" nations, 50, 53–54; new nations, 8–9; U.S.S.R., 81–83, 86–89, 91; U.S., 76; Western Europe, 63–64, 66, 71, 72
Berlin, East, 61
British Royal Society, 32, 40
British Royal Society of Arts and Manufactures, 33
Bronowski, J., 32
Burma, 7
Bush, Vannevar, 73

Cabinet posts for science, 69–70
Capital requirements, in new nations, 21–23
Catherine the Great, 88
Caulker, Solomon, 37
Central Aerodynamics Research Institute, U.S.S.R., 81
Central Treaty Organization (CENTO), 56
Ceylon, 7
Ch'en Yi, 98
China, Nationalist, 22, 92, 93
China, People's Republic of, 23, 40, 62; Academica Sinica, 98, 99–101; basic research, 96–97, 105; Eighth Congress of Communist Party, 99; electric power, 94; governmental organization of science, 98–99, 100–101; "Great Leap Forward," 93; liberalism of science in, 100, 104–105; manpower, 95, 99–100; meteorology, 94; mineral resources, 93–94; Planning Committee for Scientific Development, 98; rift with U.S.S.R., 7, 102–104; scientific education, 95–96; scientific philosophy, 97–99, 104–105; scientific tradition, lack of, 97–98, 104; Soviet aid to, 98–99, 101–103; Soviet influence on science, 94–95, 98–101; status of science, 92, 94–95, 96–97; status of technology, 92–94; steel production, 93; technological tradition, 30, 92–93, 98; Twelve Year Science

Publications of the Council on Foreign Relations

FOREIGN AFFAIRS (quarterly), edited by Hamilton Fish Armstrong.

THE UNITED STATES IN WORLD AFFAIRS (annual). Volumes for 1931, 1932 and 1933, by Walter Lippmann and William O. Scroggs; for 1934–1935, 1936, 1937, 1938, 1939 and 1940, by Whitney H. Shepardson and William O. Scroggs; for 1945–1947, 1947–1948 and 1948–1949, by John C. Campbell; for 1949, 1950, 1951, 1952, 1953 and 1954, by Richard P. Stebbins; for 1955, by Hollis W. Barber; for 1956, 1957, 1958, 1959, 1960, 1961 and 1962, by Richard P. Stebbins.

DOCUMENTS ON AMERICAN FOREIGN RELATIONS (annual). Volume for 1952 edited by Clarence W. Baier and Richard P. Stebbins; for 1953 and 1954, edited by Peter V. Curl; for 1955, 1956, 1957, 1958 and 1959, edited by Paul E. Zinner; for 1960, 1961 and 1962, edited by Richard P. Stebbins.

POLITICAL HANDBOOK AND ATLAS OF THE WORLD (annual), edited by Walter H. Mallory.

AFRICA: A Foreign Affairs Reader, edited by Philip W. Quigg.

THE PHILIPPINES AND THE UNITED STATES: Problems of Partnership, by George E. Taylor.

SOUTHEAST ASIA IN UNITED STATES POLICY, by Russell H. Fifield.

UNESCO: ASSESSMENT AND PROMISE, by George N. Shuster.

THE PEACEFUL ATOM IN FOREIGN POLICY, by Arnold Kramish.

THE ARABS AND THE WORLD: Nasser's Arab Nationalist Policy, by Charles D. Cremeans.

TOWARD AN ATLANTIC COMMUNITY, by Christian A. Herter.

THE SOVIET UNION, 1922–1962: A Foreign Affairs Reader, edited by Philip E. Mosely.

THE POLITICS OF FOREIGN AID: American Experience in Southeast Asia, by John D. Montgomery.

SPEARHEADS OF DEMOCRACY: Labor in the Developing Countries, by George C. Lodge.

LATIN AMERICA: Diplomacy and Reality, by Adolf A. Berle.

THE ORGANIZATION OF AMERICAN STATES AND THE HEMISPHERE CRISIS, by John C. Dreier.

THE UNITED NATIONS: Structure for Peace, by Ernest A. Gross.

THE LONG POLAR WATCH: Canada and the Defense of North America, by Melvin Conant.

Publications of the Council on Foreign Relations

ARMS AND POLITICS IN LATIN AMERICA (Revised Edition), by Edwin Lieuwen.

THE FUTURE OF UNDERDEVELOPED COUNTRIES: Political Implications of Economic Development (Revised Edition), by Eugene Staley.

SPAIN AND DEFENSE OF THE WEST: Ally and Liability, by Arthur P. Whitaker.

SOCIAL CHANGE IN LATIN AMERICA TODAY: Its Implications for United States Policy, by Richard N. Adams, John P. Gillin, Allan R. Holmberg, Oscar Lewis, Richard W. Patch, and Charles W. Wagley.

FOREIGN POLICY: THE NEXT PHASE: The 1960s (Revised Edition), by Thomas K. Finletter.

DEFENSE OF THE MIDDLE EAST: Problems of American Policy (Revised Edition), by John C. Campbell.

COMMUNIST CHINA AND ASIA: Challenge to American Policy, by A. Doak Barnett.

FRANCE, TROUBLED ALLY: De Gaulle's Heritage and Prospects, by Edgar S. Furniss, Jr.

THE SCHUMAN PLAN: A Study in Economic Cooperation, 1950–1959, by William Diebold, Jr.

SOVIET ECONOMIC AID: The New Aid and Trade Policy in Underdeveloped Countries, by Joseph S. Berliner.

RAW MATERIALS: A Study of American Policy, by Percy W. Bidwell.

NATO AND THE FUTURE OF EUROPE, by Ben T. Moore.

AFRICAN ECONOMIC DEVELOPMENT, by William Hance.

INDIA AND AMERICA: A Study of Their Relations, by Phillips Talbot and S. L. Poplai.

JAPAN BETWEEN EAST AND WEST, by Hugh Borton, Jerome B. Cohen, William J. Jorden, Donald Keene, Paul F. Langer and C. Martin Wilbur.

NUCLEAR WEAPONS AND FOREIGN POLICY, by Henry A. Kissinger.

MOSCOW-PEKING AXIS: Strengths and Strains, by Howard L. Boorman, Alexander Eckstein, Philip E. Mosely and Benjamin Schwartz.

RUSSIA AND AMERICA: Dangers and Prospects, by Henry L. Roberts.

FOREIGN AFFAIRS BIBLIOGRAPHY, 1942–1952, by Henry L. Roberts.